A Life in Forestry

John McEwen

Edited by Doris Hatvany

Perth and Kinross Libraries

First Published 1998

ISBN 0 905452 24 0

Published by
Perth and Kinross Libraries

Printed by
Cordfall Ltd
0141 332 4640

Contents

Foreword

JOHN MCEWEN IS BEST KNOWN for his book *Who Owns Scotland* (1977). This showed in detail for the first time in a hundred years, how most of Scotland's land is still owned by a few hundred landowners with substantial private estates.

Who Owns Scotland caused quite a stir when it was first published. And twenty years later, much of the momentum that now exists for land reform to be amongst the first legislation in the new Scottish Parliament, can be traced back to the influence of that book.

A Life in Forestry provides a fascinating insight into John McEwen and his long life up until his 97th year. Remarkably, John McEwen lived for another 8 years and continued actively engaged in research on landownership until the last couple of years of his life, when he never recovered from the blow of the death of his wife Margaret.

In September 1993, one year after John died, the first "John McEwen Memorial Lecture on Land Tenure in Scotland" was held in Aberfeldy a few miles from his birthplace in Keltneyburn. The McEwen Lectures were started as a tribute to John's life and work and have developed into a successful and influential series of annual Lectures, as reflected by the Fifth McEwen Lecture in September 1998 being delivered by the Secretary of State for Scotland to a capacity audience of 300 people.

Other recent developments have also given John McEwen a continuing presence in the land reform debate. These include Andy Wightman's widely read book *Who Owns Scotland*, published in 1996 and dedicated to John McEwen, and the launch of the McEwen Archive by Perth and Kinross Libraries, the publishers of this book. The archive, which stores John McEwen's own papers, is also being developed as a reference collection of material published about landownership in Scotland.

John McEwen's long life from the 1880s to the 1990s meant that he provided an extraordinary link between personal experience of the harshness of Victorian landownership in the Highlands and the modern debate for land reform. Some of his views may now seem dated, for example, the case for land nationalisation espoused in *Who Owns Scotland* and his anti-devolution stance in the debate at that time. However, it was the man himself and not his views that have made John McEwen such a figurehead for today's land reform movement. As this book shows, he was deeply committed to promoting the common good and improving the well-being of his fellow human beings.

John had strongly held views. However, amongst his many admirable attributes was his continuing quest, even beyond the age of 100, to improve his knowledge and understanding and to continue to develop his own views. A particular example was the way, in his latter years, he came to recognise that it was local, not simply national, community control that held the key to ensuring that Scotland's land was used for the benefit of the people of Scotland.

There was nothing romantic or misty eyed about John's views about how the land should be managed. His own hard life ensured that. Yet the forthright way he tended to express his views should never be allowed to distract from his compassion and humanity – as anyone who enjoyed the warmth and hospitality of John and Margaret McEwen's friendship will also readily testify.

Robin Callander

Introduction

JOHN MCEWEN'S LIFELONG INTEREST in landownership, his left-wing socialist aspirations and his choice of a career in forestry were shaped by his early experiences. His grandfather had a small hill farm and a large family, with the result that the family had to be dispersed. John's father went into forestry, and became shepherd-forester to a big landowner. Conditions there, the contrast between the lives and living conditions of employees and employer and the treatment of the tenants shaped much of his later thinking, and resulted some three-quarters of a century later in his pioneering work, *Who Owns Scotland?* His views were reinforced by his employment in forestry, which took him to the north of Scotland, Wales, Ireland and finally to Perthshire, a county he knew intimately and for which he had great affection.

His early experiences also contributed to his lively interest in politics. His father, like many working men of the time, had been a Liberal, according to John on the more radical wing of the party, and his closest friends in Glasgow, where he was sent to school, were also radical Liberals. Round about 1910 John bought a pamphlet by Ramsay MacDonald, which introduced him to Labour ideas, and soon after that he began buying Tom Johnston's rather eccentric weekly paper, the *Glasgow Forward*. He was also influenced by Johnston's *Our Scots Noble Families*, though he does not seem to have heard of the author's *History of the Working Classes in Scotland*. In 1918, when the Labour Party constitution was altered and individual members were admitted, he joined the Party, and came in contact with leading Scottish labour activists like John Paton and Joe Duncan; John very much admired the latter in particular.

John worked for the Forestry Commission from its inception in 1919 and did much to encourage trade unionism among forestry workers and improve pay and conditions. His links with the Workers' Union and with forestry workers south of the Border had two consequences: a certain amount of victimisation and a strong dislike of devolution. If devolution came about the McEwens declared themselves ready to move to England. He was the prime mover in setting up the Royal Scottish Forestry Society and was instrumental, when he worked in Moray, in starting courses for forestry workers. He had an intense interest in education for forestry, being always very conscious of his inadequate education (more so than was necessary, as he had taken many evening classes, cycling miles after a hard day's work, and was widely read). Though his OBE did not impress him, he was always very proud of his election as President of the Royal Scottish Forestry Society, a position held until that time by big landowners like the Duke of Buccleuch and the Earl of Dundee.

In 1950 John and his first wife, Belle, settled in Rosemount, Blairgowrie, and he became involved in Labour Party activities. After his second marriage, to Margaret Miller, whom I had known well in Aberdeen, as we were both active in the Fabian and Humanist Societies, John became more involved in Labour politics. In 1971 Margaret, Jim Ferguson, Alistair Steven and John researched and wrote the pamphlet *The Acreocracy of Perthshire*, which sold well. He also contributed to the *Red Paper on Scotland* and finally in 1977 published his most important work *Who Owns Scotland?*, which was reprinted some 18 months later in a format and with addenda which did not please him.

In his youth John had been deeply religious, and in Glasgow and Edinburgh had taken part in slum missions. Later he became a convinced atheist (agnostic was a term he could not condone, as "hedging one's bets"). Like many Labour activists he was a strict teetotaller, though he did not force this view on his family and friends.

As I have said, I had known Margaret Miller well when we both lived in Aberdeen. After her marriage, which I considered a romantic but also a brave step, as she was 61 and John 80, we kept only loosely in touch, especially as I has moved to SW Scotland. In 1976 I went for a visit to the McEwens in their little wood-panelled house in Rosemount, and became accepted as a family friend. John and Margaret were very happy in their marriage, and I paid them frequent visits. John, despite his age, still drove his car, doing so until his early nineties, and we travelled all about Perthshire. I realised what a fund of local knowledge John possessed and I discussed the possibility of tape-recording his memories. John at first demurred, but then became very excited at the prospect, and I stayed with them for several weeks in 1984-85 to carry out the project. John also took the opportunity to persuade me – unsuccessfully – to join the

Labour Party, so as to work within the Party for left-wing politics. At that time he was reading the *West Highland Free Press*, *Marxism Today*, which he considered indispensable and for which he had abandoned *Tribune*, and various local and national papers. A number of interesting people also visited. In spite of all these distractions, at the age of 98 his energy was extraordinary; we recorded in the morning, later in the afternoon, and, after his nightly game of Scrabble with Margaret, who was a crossword buff and almost invariably won, we began again at 9 or 10 p.m. In this way we completed eighteen 90-minute tapes, which we had typed and sent to his publisher. Polygon considered his autobiography too detailed for publication, John refused to make any cuts, and this stalemate continued for many years.

John's death in 1992, two days before his 105th birthday, and the institution of the McEwen lectures have led to increased interest in his life, and it is hoped that this short book will be an introduction to one who was a Socialist, trade unionist, forester, pioneer of land reform, and on a more personal note, a kind and helpful friend.

Doris Hatvany

Note: This work is transcribed from the tapes of John McEwen. As far as possible places, dates, family names, etc. have been checked, but is still likely that some errors remain.

The eighteen tapes are deposited in the John McEwen archive in the AK Bell Library, Perth.

Chapter 1

Boyhood in the Strath

I COME FROM A PERTHSHIRE FAMILY. My McEwen great-grandfather belonged to Killin, where he opened up a lime-kiln locally, producing lime for agricultural use. From there he went to Lochearnhead, renting the small farm of Castran. My grandfather, the eldest son, took over the farm and had a family of five sons and three daughters, of whom my father was, I think, the second oldest son. Castran was not a big farm, and not at all fertile: it was a hill farm, giving a very poor living for the tenant. I met my grandfather only once or twice. I remember him as an old, kindly, very friendly gentleman. There was no living on the farm for all the family, and they had to scatter. My father went into forestry, and became shepherd-forester to Sir Donald Currie, the millionaire shipping owner, at Garth Castle in Glen Lyon. This meant the break-up of the farm, as my father was the one who had kept it going.

My father was an unusual person. He had become precentor of the Free Church of Scotland in Lochearnhead, but lost all connection with Lochearnhead when he moved to Garth Castle, a big change for him from life as a small independent farmer to being under the domination of landlordism. My mother, whom he met in Lochearnhead, was maid to the minister, a Mr Findlater, who was well known in Scotland for the strong stand he had taken against the Clearances when he was minister in Sutherland. He was one of the ministers who had broken away from the Church of Scotland in 1843. He had two daughters, who later wrote novels published in Scotland. Living in this home my mother became a keen reader, with a retentive memory. She seemed to know Sir Walter Scott's novels inside out. After their marriage my father and she came to live on Garth estate, at first in rooms, then later in a house newly built by Sir Donald Currie, who wanted to give the impression of caring about his workpeople and their welfare. He built reading and recreation rooms, with this house attached. It had an upstairs bedroom with only a skylight window, and downstairs a small kitchen with a bed in it – that was the whole house. It was built in a very dangerous position, especially for a family with small children, set on the side of the Keltney Burn, with a steep slope down to the burn itself. There was only a grass path, up which every drop of water used in the house had to be carried, even when my mother was carrying me. Even when I was quite young I thought it dreadful that a millionaire should build a new castle for himself and a house like that for his workers. His own home was a very extensive mansion, with stabling and outbuildings and all the appurtenances of a mansion house.

The reading room, which was well supplied with books, must have been important to my mother as a relief from the misery and uncomfortable life she had to put up with. She also, even when she was pregnant, did a certain amount of washing for the better off.

I lived there until I was seven years old, when my father got an appointment on an estate in Argyllshire, belonging to John MacLachlan, and we went there in July, I think, of 1895. On the way we stayed one night with a sister of my mother's, who had a small shop in Pollokshields in Glasgow, and the next morning caught the Lord Broomielaw in Glasgow to Inveraray. We got off at Strachur, the pier for Strathlachlan, and were met by some form of transport which took us to the cottage where my father and mother were to live for the next twenty-five years or so.

The house at Garth had been new and clean; the one we went to at Castle Lachlan was derelict and rat-ridden. Currie had been one of the new moneyed class, the MacLachlans were an old family. John MacLachlan was chief of the clan, and very proud of it. But the house he offered his overseer, a man who was going to have a certain amount of responsibility, was quite scandalous. The castle and its surrounds were even more rat-ridden. I can never forget the sight of the hundreds of rats, disease-ridden, the ugliest things I have ever seen, running all over the stables and outbuildings. One of the first things my father did was to get a trapper from Glasgow who came for a fortnight and cleared the lot. MacLachlan was a lawyer in Edinburgh, but he came periodically to the castle and his mother and four or five brothers and sisters lived there almost all the time. MacLachlan must have seen these rats, but did nothing about them. The trapper did not come to our place, but my brother and I trapped the rats and cleared them out.

We lived there on a small croft, which was part of my father's wage from the estate. It had quite a good garden and about a couple of acres of very poor land, sufficient for grazing a cow, with additional grazing on adjoining land belonging to a local farmer. Strathlachlan was a crofting community, with some thirty to forty crofts on it. It was a long strath, running from the castle or school in Strathlachlan to Otter Ferry, about twelve miles long and about 12,000 acres. It ran nearly all the way alongside Loch Fyne. There were crofting communities of perhaps three or four crofts at Stuckreoch and Leachd – both Gaelic names – and a bigger crofting community of seven, eight or nine crofts at Newton. There were two or three crofts at Sunfield, where in no time a Post Office was set up with a telephone. When we went there, there was no Post Office. Down to Otter Ferry it was less populated. There was a small croft at Inver, where the Strathlachlan River entered Loch Fyne, quite near the castle itself which stood on a beautiful broad flat piece of land looking on to Loch Fyne. The Inver was quite near too, where the MacLachlans' yacht was kept. There was one more croft, and after that nothing, until from Strachur on there were a few farms – Letters farm, a fairly big farm on reasonably good land, and Leanach, fifty-fifty upland and hill farming, quite a valuable farm with a reasonable number of cattle and sheep but, like the others, not fully developed. Strone was a small hill farm, but the next farm, Feorline, was quite a big farm with a considerable area of flat tillage land. We lived on the edge of it and were in close contact with it. The really big farm on the estate had been formed out of two farms, Barnacarry and Lephinmore. It had some good tillage land with a considerable area of upland, carrying two shepherds, which meant it was really quite a big farm. Further down the Strath was the last farm on the estate, Lephinchapel, and one or two houses. Apart from one other farm somewhat detached from the Strath, that was the picture of the Strath. It is now largely depopulated. There was very little forestry on the estate, though near our house there was one fair-sized plantation. Our house was in a small clachan, which included the school, the schoolmaster's house and our croft, with below it the smithy and a lodge where the gamekeeper stayed.

The Stuckreoch and Leachd crofters, and the crofters at Inver, were fishermen as well. They formed a more prosperous community in the Strath; from about 1905, when we went there, to 1914 they were all quite well-off. Then the herring fishing failed, and today I don't think there's a croft left. Darling in his book on the Highlands refers to Strathlachlan as being a crofting community. In many ways it was, but it seemed to have no deep-seated feeling of community the way crofting communities in the real crofting counties have had.

Strathlachlan was an entirely Gaelic-speaking Strath. My father had Gaelic but the rest of us didn't speak it. As a result, and because my father took the place of a Highlander, being from Perthshire and not even from Argyllshire, we were looked upon as complete outsiders. I left the Strath when I was 12 to go to school in Glasgow, so I don't know just how long it took, but it must have been twelve to fifteen years before we were accepted. In school, though we were the only English-speaking people, Gaelic was never used; I do not remember ever hearing the children in that school speaking Gaelic. But there was no ill-feeling inside the school. The ill-feeling was outside, particularly towards my father, I suppose because he had taken the job from a Highlander.

The community was divided in a way by the Church. There were two churches, the Auld Kirk, run by a minister from Strachur, and the Free Church, which also had a small church in Strachur. Both ministers lived in Strachur, but there was an Auld Kirk in Strathlachlan where the minister preached every Sunday, or perhaps every second Sunday. There was no Free Church, the services were held in the school, I think fortnightly, but the minister visited us very frequently and was very friendly with us. The division by church, however, was not very serious.

Apart from church attendance there was very little community life, no entertainment or anything of that kind. It was a very quiet-living little community, except on New Year's Day. Two functions took place on that day. A shinty match took place on the forenoon, played on a field adjoining the castle, which brought the men of the community together. The women did not go along to those matches, but every man and boy appeared. Then on New Year's Eve there was a dance in the school which brought the entire community together. I was too young to go, but we used to sneak along and try to see in through the windows. That didn't get us very far – I don't remember seeing anything at all. There was no doubt a good deal of drinking, but this was not a very heavy-drinking community. There were a good many teetotallers in the Strath at the time, both among the fishermen and the crofters. Christmas was not celebrated publicly: at home we had a small celebration and exchanged Christmas cards, but there was nothing of moment. There were no other holidays. We knew about the Glasgow holidays when people invaded Strathlachlan, but we had only the one day at New Year. I experienced this later in life too, not only in the Strath but in the north of Scotland. Recreation in the Strath was thus very limited. The fishermen were tied up with fishing for about six months of the year, and in the winter they had to put their skiffs in order, and at the same time they had their crofts to look after. There was a yachting craze among the aristocrats at the time, and the younger boys worked on the yachts for a few months, but this did not affect the married people.

One recreation I did have in the Strath was trout fishing. Today I wouldn't fish for trout, I am totally against blood sports, but then I found great joy in fishing either in the small burn which we would fish at any time, or in a bigger burn where the salmon and sea trout came up. We were restricted there, but we used to sneak down and try it. I was very keen, later on, on upstream small-worm fishing, and could pick up two or three dozen trout at a time in that way. Only one other person, a crofter's son, took advantage of the trout fishing. The salmon fishing was kept strictly for the laird, who was an absentee landlord. The MacLachlan family were not at all helpful to the community. They took the hefty rents, which in addition to the income MacLachlan had from his work in J. & F. Anderson's in Edinburgh made him a wealthy man.

Apart from the minister and the laird, the only other important figure in the community was the doctor, who came on his visits by horse and trap. He lived in Strachur, six miles away, but we never had any difficulty in getting him. We called him in as little as possible, of course, because we had to pay him.

Though life in the Strath seems to us now very limited, we did have contact with the outside world. As regards newspapers, other people might have got a weekly, I'm not sure about that, but we were perhaps more forward-looking. We got the *Glasgow Herald*, I think twice a week, and the *People's Friend* and *People's Journal*. I doubt very much if daily papers were very much read at that time.

The postal services were quite good and reliable. There was a postman, Sandy MacLachlan, who must have been in that job for thirty to forty years. There was a pillar-box at the end of the school, and the postman went from Leachd, where he lived, to Strachur on foot in the morning and collected the mail from there at 7 o'clock. Then he delivered the whole way down the Strath to the castle, beyond which he did not go. I don't know how Lephinmore and Lephinchapel got their letters, perhaps the farmers collected them at the Post Office. The postman walked from Leachd to Strachur, then down the whole glen, coming to us between 3 and 4 in the afternoon. Then he went on to the castle and stayed there till 5 o'clock. He would get a cup of tea there, then return and collect from the pillar-box at the school. There were two despatches in the day. He later came by bicycle and arrived a couple of hours earlier.

15

The telegraph service did not come in till we were there for a few years when the Telegraph and Post Office was opened at Sunfield, halfway between our house and Newton. The wires caused such damage to grouse that special appliances had to be put on the wires to let the grouse see where they were, otherwise "the 12th" might have suffered.

In Strachur there were four grocers' shops, of which only one was licensed. One was a baker, who baked the most terrible bread you ever tasted. We had excellent supplies, a van came practically every day from Dunoon, 20 miles away. Since the van was, like the others, horse-drawn, it had to stay overnight at the smithy and go back to Dunoon in the morning. It carried alcohol, ostensibly on order. Whisky was sold in big bottles, costing 3/6 at the time. All the crofters had their own milk. When the cows went dry I suppose they would supply each other. We had the one cow, and when she went dry we had to go to Feorline Farm and buy our milk there, and sometimes butter. My mother, like the other women, baked scones and oatcakes; the small shop in Newton supplied bread – Glasgow bread. We grew all the things we needed, potatoes, vegetables, fruit. At that time, and perhaps it's the same yet, people in the Highlands, crofters particularly, were very loath to grow fruit. We had always grown a certain amount of small fruit, but when I went back to work in the Botanic Gardens in Edinburgh I found the finest blackcurrants there. I took cuttings and sent them home, and the finest blackcurrants I ever saw grew in my father's garden. But that was not usual in the Strath.

Fish could not be bought at any time, all marketing was external, except for the herring which people stored for winter. In the autumn we killed a pig for winter use and a small sheep, and they were salted like the herrings. In the summer we had butcher meat from the vans and rabbits could be got. My mother kept a lot of hens and they were frequently killed off and used. If a visitor arrived unexpectedly for a meal, a hen could be killed. My mother in the spring of every year reared ducks which were extremely popular with the laird's people and she sold them for a fair bit of money.

When we were quite young my mother made a lot of our clothes. I wore the kilt – there wasn't a kilt to be seen anywhere in the Highlands, but we came from Perthshire and wore the kilt – for some years at school we were the "kiltie cauld bums" of that corner. Suits and other clothes came from outside; there were no clothiers in Strachur, Inveraray was the nearest centre, but the finest trousers we wore came from Glasgow. My mother never bought kilts, but trousers came from outside sources.

16

My mother was a remarkable woman. She was a keen reader, and must have led the community in two things: she was the first or second person to have a bicycle, and the first person to buy a piano, and that piano revolutionised our lives. My mother could not play, but my sister Madge learned to play a bit. Both my parents were musical. My mother was a very good singer, and knew a great many songs, Scottish songs and popular airs. My father, as I have said, was precentor in the Free Church in Lochearnhead. He could sing very well, in Gaelic, and even late on in his life we used to ask him to give us one of his Gaelic songs. In Lochearnhead Church the service was in English, though it was a Gaelic-speaking countryside, and my father when he went to school couldn't speak English. The congregation in Lochearnhead must have appreciated his singing because when he left they presented him with a small lap desk, a beautiful piece of furniture, and I wish I had been able to inherit it, and have it in my possession, but I do not know what happened to it.

There were two jobs I used to get. One was in the summertime, when Feorline Farm was clipping the sheep. It had a big number of sheep, with three or four men clipping, and I had to stamp an identification mark on the sheep after it was clipped. This was done with tar and an iron with "S" (in the case of Feorline) on it. The other job was at the grouse shooting. There were no butts then, so the men had to walk in a strip with two game-keepers, perhaps half a dozen guns and dogs who pointed out each covey. My brother and I for a couple of seasons had to take the dogs, of which there were two sets; when one got tired the other had to follow on. There were only two dogs on each lead because they used to scrap. I knew one boy who had four or five dogs in a van and when he was driving home alone the dogs began to fight and he was badly hurt trying to control them.

I had one particular friend in the Strath whom I lost very early. We lived next door to the gamekeeper, a man called Donald Macmillan, from Kintyre, who lived in the Lodge Gate. Opposite him was the smithy and the Kirk. The smithy was a quite valuable croft with a good deal of low-tillage land, rented by a man called Archie Crawford, with whose second son, also called Archie, I became very friendly; we were very fond of each other. However, Donald Macmillan and Archie Crawford didn't get on at all, and David Macmillan, son of Donald, reported Archie Crawford as having a pheasant in one of his rabbit snares. He had the right to snare rabbits, but nothing else, and David Macmillan reported this to the laird, John MacLachlan, who ruthlessly cleared out poor Archie and his family. They had to flit to Craignish near Oban, miles away from

17

us, and I had no chance of ever seeing Archie again. This was one of the sad things in my life. The pheasant had been placed in the snare by the gamekeeper himself – I am certain of this now – because within a few weeks a new family came in, Bannatynes from the Kintyre district, one of whose daughters the gamekeeper shortly afterwards married. He also tried one filthy trick on me. Willie, my brother, and I were set to work on the 12th but Macmillan one year got a nephew of his to come for a holiday to the smithy, and I was told I was not required. My mother tackled Broad, the shooting tenant, a London financier, and I was kept on. I've known gamekeepers all of my life – I know them from the north of Scotland to the south – and they're all tarred with the same stick – their support for the laird is impossible to fathom. The loss of Archie Crawford from the school was one of the biggest tragedies of my life.

Chapter 2

Schooldays

WHEN I WAS FOUR OR FIVE I WENT to school, walking two and a half miles to Fortingall. We had a woman teacher there, a Miss Menzies, one of the most kindly women I have ever had any contact with. The head teacher was said to be somewhat brutal, but I was never under him. I left when I was seven, and apart from the friendliness of Miss Menzies I don't remember much about my early education.

At school in the Strath the only thing I remember is the arithmetic class. There were three or four of us at the same level, two girls, another boy and myself, amongst the oldest in the school then. The boy was a shepherd's son and a bit dull. The two girls, I think, were Lily Robertson, a shepherd's daughter from Strone Farm where he was in charge of the farm, a very clever girl, and the other was a girl MacLachlan, also very clever. She was the daughter of one of the crofting/fishing people. I was very sorry when I was separated from them. This happened because Lorne District Council, or whatever it was called at that time, instituted a series of bursaries which started in 1899 when I was eleven. There was no examination. I don't know how the selection was made, possibly by the teacher, and I was selected. The bursary was for £12 a year for three years. I went to Glasgow on the Lord of the Isles, and started school on 1st September. It was a shock to a boy coming from a quiet school in the country to a posh fee-paying school in Glasgow, the Albert Road School. I landed in a class of 30 to 40 boys, but I wasn't lost for long. I soon got to know the boys, and became friendly with one or two. One was a boy Gray, who in the end became a minister of the Gospel. I don't know if that was what attracted me, but I was blatantly religious at that time. I used to wear a Christian Endeavour Badge and attend the twice-weekly class which was held on Mondays and Saturdays from about 7 to 8 o'clock. It was a deeply religious small section of the church and I enjoyed it.

My closest friend of all the boys in the school was Willie McArthur, whose aunt was at one time in the Academy, though I never had her as a teacher, she taught the girls. It was a mixed school, and from the second year on there were mixed classes, but I didn't get to know any of the girls at all – I didn't keep clear of them, but they were posh and I was out-and-out working class. Willie and I didn't bother with the girls at Christian Endeavour either, though there were girls I would have liked very much to get to know. I don't know what drew Willie and me together, he wasn't a member of the church I went to. The aunt with whom I stayed was a member of Well's Church, *the* posh church in Pollokshields. The Christian Endeavour meeting there was at one time under the charge of Willie's aunt, and it was there that Willie and I became close friends. He was brainy, he must have seized most of the prizes in the Second and Third Years when I was at school. Why he was attracted to me I don't know, it may have been the association with Christian Endeavour.

My aunt had a dairy and my day's work began at 6 o'clock when I had to get up and deliver milk from 6 to 8 in the morning. Then I got ready for school, and spent my day from 9 o'clock to 4 p.m. in school. I also had to do an afternoon milk delivery between 4 and 5, which was quite usual in Glasgow at that time. It was a seven day week too. Many a time I could have gone on strike, but I would have to go home, and that would have meant the end of my education.

My aunt, a Miss Mary Dow, had a shop at 170 Darnley Street, in Pollokshields, Glasgow. It had a frontage of one large plate-glass window, with a display to attract the children from Melville Street School, just round the corner, who invaded the narrow passage along the counter to make their purchases. This passage led to a large room at the back where in a big sink milk cans were thoroughly washed. It had a coal-fired grate for cooking food, with a large table and chairs for meals during the day.

All kinds of scones and pancakes were sold in the shop, baked in a small narrow section partitioned off from the back kitchen. The demand for scones was quite considerable. There was also a constant sale of fresh country eggs, the usual shop eggs at that time were "terrible", and the demand for these could not be met. The eggs came through my grandmother in Blackford and I had to go weekly to collect quite a large box of these from Buchanan Street Station by tram, newly changed from horse to electric power. I did the same periodically to pick up the children's sweeties from the town wholesalers. One further job at the end of the week was helping a second frail aunt in the back shop to peel potatoes for Saturday's potato scones.

In a way I suppose I had some joy in all my work at "170", but many a time I craved for cricket or football in both of which I was fairly competent. Home life in the evenings and on Sundays was really enjoyed, away from the toils of shop, milk delivery and so on, in a quite spacious house one stair up in the adjoining close.

I don't say I made much headway at school. I was far behind the others in my previous education, I wasn't ambitious, and I wasn't clever. I was at the bottom of the class all the time, or as near the bottom as didn't matter. When I started at the Albert Road School there was just an elementary department, but in my second year they had managed to build up a science side and we had a choice. I took science but Johnny Gray, who was my closest pal at that time, chose the other side and we got separated, almost like Archie Crawford and myself, although, unlike Archie and myself, Johnny and I did meet occasionally afterwards and became quite friendly in later life. However, I was paired off with big, tall Billy Lindsay, who was top of the class all the time. The teacher must have thought Billy Lindsay would help me. I don't know what happened to him. I was never very close with another boy, Andy Robb, who lived around the corner from us and whose mother was one of our customers, but I always liked him and followed his career. He became a Professor of Naval Architecture in Glasgow University. Later, when I was writing a lot to the *Glasgow Herald*, he wrote me to say he was watching the *Glasgow Herald* for my letters and was very appreciative of them.

My aunt was extremely religious, a great mission worker in the slums. She wasn't satisfied with going to one set of slums, she went to two and I had to accompany her. She went to the Gorbals, and to a place in Kinning Park which shouldn't have been a slum, having been built for top-grade working men. It had become invaded by Irish and by Highlanders, and had declined. I got to know the poorest section of the Gorbals. The Mission Hall, attached to the church I should think, was somewhere near Rose Street and Thistle Street, and it was in these streets that my aunt did her mission work. The great majority of the people there were Roman Catholics. One of my main recollections of these visits was coming home on a Saturday or Sunday night to the perfume of kippering. There must have been a kipperer's there, and the smell of kippers being smoked remains in my nostrils yet. In spite of living under landlordism in the Strath and seeing the Gorbals at first hand, I wasn't interested in politics yet. I was fourteen when I left school and the church was my line: I was a church worker.

The day I left school I felt a depth of sadness which I have never forgotten. To think that I was finished with my education! I still remember coming out of that school and saying, "Well, I'm finished, what a pity, why couldn't I go on?" Though I started secondary school with the disadvantage of a poor education in a small village school, I ended with a sound grounding in Arithmetic, a subject I was good at, and I did reasonably well in Chemistry and Physics, a foundation I was able to build on later. I also read a great deal. I have already mentioned that my mother was a keen reader, and that had a great influence on me. At school in Glasgow we had a wide range of books, some interesting, some boring, which we had to read at home and write about. One of the set books which I found extremely boring was Kingsley's *Hereward the Wake*. Another set book was *Robinson Crusoe* – that was totally different and I did enjoy it very much. There were other books which we read or studied at home: Longfellow, Gray's *Elegy in a Country Churchyard*, and we had one Shakespeare play which I do remember, *The Merchant of Venice*. I enjoyed the play, especially the part where the Jew is told, "You must not spill one drop of blood"; that remains in my mind. Outside school I had other interests in reading. There were several weeklies at that time. The *Boy's Own Paper* was published as a weekly at 1d a time, but was also published as a monthly, the four issues being bound into one book. It had not only the written matter of the weekly, but had a beautiful illustrated picture page. This cost ½d more. The monthly cost was 4½d, and I thought the extra ½d certainly worth while.

Besides the *Boy's Own Paper* which I got monthly I did have a weekly, *Chums*. The *Boy's Own Paper* was a more solid kind of thing with a good deal of information in it as well as enjoyable reading, but *Chums* was more extreme. It wasn't bloodthirsty by any manner of means, but it tended in that direction, and it filled a good deal of my life because I read it very closely. Similar to it, but more extreme, though still not bloodthirsty, was the *Boy's Friend*. A friend of mine, Leonard Duncan, read that type of paper too – I can't remember its name – and we exchanged papers. I also read two other monthlies, heavier stuff, one of which was the *Strand Magazine*, which my uncle took. The other was *The Wide, Wide World*. I got it from the gardener in Strathlachlan, John Wesley, who was a very able gardener but, sad to say, a very heavy drinker. *The Wide, Wide World* had more adventurous content than the *Strand*. Looking back, I see that I was reading widely at that stage, and this must have formed the basis of my future extensive reading.

There was one incident which rather annoyed me at the time. Willie McArthur's mother gave me *Lorna Doone* to read, and I was enthralled by it. My aunt, who was very strict, enjoying only religious matter, took exception to *Lorna Doone* and I had to take it back to Mrs McArthur. I don't know what exception she could have taken to it, but soon I got hold of it on my own and enjoyed it very much indeed.

Just before I went to Cullen to take up a career in forestry, in 1905, I was introduced to another weekly. The Strath was very attractive and brought in many holidaymakers, among them three young women, sisters, two of whom were schoolteachers, while the other kept house for them. We became very friendly with them, and the oldest one, Alice, suggested that instead of what I had been reading I should take *T.P.'s Weekly*, a much more solid periodical, dealing with politics, than I had been reading. I read that magazine for ten or fifteen years after that. In one of these issues a serial by Jack London was begun, *White Fang*, and, when at midday in the forest we took an hour off to eat our packed lunch, I literally devoured that story. I simply itched every week until *T.P.'s Weekly* came out and I could continue with *White Fang*, just as we had itched to continue the readings my mother held from the *People's Friend* when we were young.

I have mentioned the piano my mother bought and Madge learned to play. My friend Willie McArthur was a skilled pianist, and one of the links between us was that we were both fond of music. I could only sing, I couldn't play an instrument at all, at any time in my life, but Willie was a first-class pianist. After school I was in Glasgow for a couple of years and during that time I visited the McArthurs' house a good deal, and he and I used to sit at the piano together, he playing and I listening, enjoying what he was playing. When we were at school together we had two months' holiday in the summer, and he used to come and stay with us for those two months. As a result of the piano coming into our house we formed a group, just of our family, the three boys and the girl, father and mother, with Willie playing the piano. We used the *Students' Song Book* and got to know a great many of these. Almost every night there was this community singing in our home, and it remains in my mind as one of the most enjoyable aspects of life at this time, this group singing with Willie at the piano.

One other type of singing has always attracted me, and that is community singing in church services. I don't go to church, but in Songs of Praise over the radio and television the one thing that moves me deeply is the old Scottish psalm

23

tunes. There is nothing I enjoy more than listening to the community singing of these old Scottish songs. The words don't matter, it is the music that really counts, and they are part of our Scottish tradition. They form too part of my childhood memories, and remain deeply ingrained in me.

Chapter 3

After School:

Forestry in Cullen and Altyre

WHEN I LEFT SCHOOL AT FOURTEEN I went home for a short time, not knowing what my future was to be. I had an easy summer for some four or five weeks, then it was decided that I should go back to Glasgow. There was no work whatever in the Strath itself. I replied to advertisements for office boys, and my first job was as an office boy in a shipping agent's office in St Stephen's Square in Glasgow. The shipping agent made out his requirements and I had to go round all the shipowners in the centre of Glasgow. I then applied for a job as a young accountant in a wholesale ironmongers and got it. I was really an invoice clerk in a busy ironmongers whose goods were manufactured in Germany and America and a German was in charge. Not merely did I have to make up invoices for material sent from this wholesale shop to all the ironmongers in Glasgow but I also had to go round collecting the money. I think I stayed under a year in the shipping office, and was paid 5/- a week. I got 7/6 a week as an invoice clerk. I wasn't satisfied, but my brother became ill and put an end to it. My father had taken charge, as overseer or manager, of Lephinmore Farm. The tenant who was in the biggest farm on the estate, Lephinmore, died and although his son was there he was not given the chance of taking over the farm. My father, who was living in Balnacoil in the forester's cottage, flitted down to Lephinmore. It was a sheep farm with a small number of Highland cattle and four milking cows, and calves. There were two shepherds on the farm, a ploughman and a loon, plus my father. There was a certain amount of work in the house, as one of the men lived there, a shepherd. The other shepherd was in a house of his own, and the ploughman lived in the bothy on his own. My brother was taken on as loon. He became seriously ill with rheumatic fever, and I was asked to come home, which I did quite gladly. But the work on the farm was extremely hard.

I had to look after the calves, and milk the cows, helped by my sister Madge. After that was done I had to go out into the field and hoe turnips, keeping up with the squad, who were old and expert. Potatoes had to be planted in the spring and later on the corn and hay had to be harvested, experience which served me well later on in life. When my brother was well enough to take over again, just at the end of 1904, I had made up my mind to go in for forestry, not to go back to the city at all. My father applied to an old mate of his, a chap McKenzie, who was the head forester in Cullen House, Seafield's property, and I was told I would get a job there. I went there at the beginning of January 1905. I had to go via Glasgow, and take the train, my first long journey in a train. We left at about 10 o'clock in the morning, and arrived at Cullen at 8 or 9 at night, on one of the coldest nights I have ever put in, bitter cold compared to Argyll or Glasgow. I was met by the forester's pony and trap which took me and my trunk to my lodgings. It was a high trap, the cold was piercing, and in the background there was the sound of heavy waves in the Bay of Cullen. I can still hear that sound when I think of that journey to my digs in Lintmill, the village where nearly all the estate workers lived, foresters and others, a mile or so from Cullen. I had a small bedroom, with a skylight window, quite comfortable, with kindly people, a married man and his wife, with two boys and a girl.

I hadn't known what I was in for, but I soon learnt. I was put into a hedging squad with two oldish men, and the three of us continued the hedging project for a year. This included cleaning ivy off houses and walls, plus a certain amount of decorative work, pruning bushes into shapes. It took us a year to cover all the hedges on Cullen estate, there were miles and miles of them, beech hedges and mixed hedges of thorn and beech; there were no conifer hedges or evergreens. It was a painful job, because you used one arm only, swinging the hedge bill for six or seven hours a day. We had to be at the starting point in the shed at 7 o'clock in the morning, and were back at 6 o'clock at night, 6 days a week. We had no half-day. The hours were shorter in the winter, but not much: we had to plough through the dark to get to the shed from which we started off. We were paid only once a month. I was paid 12/- a week for my first year, with an increase of 2/- a week the second year. 14/- was the maximum for a working man at that time, and Cullen House paid better than some of the other landlords in the north of Scotland. Married people got 14/- plus a house, rent free. Some of the other landlords paid less, like the Duke of Richmond and Gordon, who was noted for his stinginess. There was also a lot of sickness caused by the way of life of the working man. Cullen House was not by any means the worst landlord.

It was an old lady who was in possession at that time, Lady Seafield, and though I worked on the estate for two years, I never saw her. She wasn't concerned with her own workers, but with the fisher folk in the fisher-town, the lower part of Cullen. Cullen was a fishing town, next door to Buckie, though not as big or rough as Buckie, and there were many accidents and losses at sea among these people.

My first year was with the hedging, my second with the fencing squad. An oldish man, Willie, was in charge, a religious man, and we got on well together. Hedging was boring, but in fencing we never knew what we were going to do from day to day: putting up a new fence, repairing somewhere else, making gates. My last job with this fencer was repairing a wooden bridge over a gully, and painting it, an interesting job, and quite new to me. But while we were on that job, about October of 1906 or 1907, Willie fell ill and died. I was left on my own for a week or two, painting the bridge, and was then transferred to what was called the felling squad, the biggest squad on the Cullen estate, consisting of four or five men plus a foreman. There were a number of squads working on the estate: the head squad, the felling squad, the fencing squad, the draining squad, policy squad, dyking squad, etc., each under their own foreman. The first two men I worked with were very likeable men, indeed I became very friendly with the foreman of the fencing squad, perhaps because we were both very religious. The next squad was far from being religious, it was the very opposite but it was what I wanted, to get some experience of the woodlands. I didn't get much. I started with the felling squad in the beginning of winter. Cullen at that time had extensive policies with old beech trees, and every winter some of these were blown down. The woodland squad had to do the clearing up, and I was put on the job of cutting off the branches and preparing the tree for sawing up and delivery to the saw mill. I wasn't long on the job, half an hour perhaps, when the five-pound axe I was handling, with my inexperience, slipped off a knot on the beech tree I was snedding on to my foot. It went through my boot, and I had practically to be carried home. The doctor was called, and I had three stitches on the top of my foot and two below with the minimum of anaesthetic. I was handicapped for about six weeks. I received my full pay, but had to pay my doctor's bill.

At least I escaped the pheasant shooting that year. I hated beating, as soaked to the skin we had to drive those pheasants, hares and rabbits into the faces of the guns, with all the suffering that entailed. That year when I was laid up one of our men was shot in the face by the factor of the estate, who was not very experienced at handling a gun. This came at the end of my term at Cullen.

In the early stages of my training at Cullen there was one particular piece of torture to which only we foresters were subjected: the annual week of carpet-beating, of every piece of floor covering the huge mansion house. Half-a-dozen of us had to beat for hour after hour for six whole days of ten hours each, huge heavy carpets slung over a wire stretched between two poles about six feet from the ground. Talk about filth, and a constant breathing of this dust, and no rest! Beer and whisky were in quite good supply each day which I suppose deadened the feelings of those youngsters like myself, as well as those of the older men, but no help at all for an eccentric individual like me, strictly teetotal, a religious lonely character such as I was. It was an absolutely unforgettable experience in the two years I was employed by this ancient Countess of Seafield.

I had enjoyed hedging and fencing, but I hadn't enjoyed the few months of felling, and when I had the chance of going to another estate, I took it, and at the beginning of 1907 I flitted from Cullen to Altyre near Forres. I had made some good friends in Cullen, who were more to my way of thinking; I was then very religious and teetotal. I was sorry to leave them; I never saw them again, but in going to Altyre I made a good move.

The estate belonged to the Gordon Cummings, descended from the old Comyn family. The laird of that time had got into trouble with King Edward VII, said to have been because of gambling or card-playing, and he was out of society altogether. Before that he had married a very rich American woman who brought money into the estate. They developed the estate with this money in a way that showed some concern for the workpeople. Pleasant houses were built, which can still be seen on the public road going from Altyre to Grantown. Up on a ridge there was a bothy, which was, in bothy-land, a palace. There was a large dining-room with a big table, and cooking facilities. Upstairs there was a dormitory for half-a-dozen beds. It was a pleasant room, it couldn't have been anything else, as the whole thing was new, but the equipment was a great improvement on anything I knew of, then or later. The foreman who was in charge had a small room to himself.

There was also a bath, but there was no hot water, though you could have a cold bath at any time.

When Gordon Cumming suffered the disgrace the men on the estate were all sent packing, but they couldn't carry on without workmen. My brother Willie and I were among the first to go into the bothy, plus an old man, a joiner and the foreman. That was the whole of what we called the outside squad. The sawmill had two or three men working on it, but my brother and I were practically alone, except for the one or two old men who did odd jobs. I look back on Altyre with the greatest of pleasure, unlike Cullen where the work was beastly. At Altyre we were really into forestry in the truest sense. At Cullen we had never planted a tree, there wasn't even a nursery, though at one time Cullen estate had led in nurseries and plantations. At Altyre our first job was planting up a new plantation, even though the estate had lowered its standards. The forester was named Robertson, not a slave-driver, but a hard man to work for. I liked him, he was straight.

Planting was not done carefully by these people. We had to get in 1000 plants a day, on rough ground, full of stones and roots, unploughed. We simply had to find a place where a plant could get in reasonably well, lift a piece of turf and stick it in, it didn't matter much how. We spent a few weeks on that, then the rest of the time my brother spent with me at Altyre, we were engaged in felling timber, and doing a certain amount of measurement. The foreman was a conceited little fellow from Cullen whom neither Willie nor I could get on with, but he left us pretty much alone. The trees were marked for us to fell, and we did the felling and cross-cutting ready for the sawmill.

Other jobs I did taught me worthwhile skills. Once was causeying (laying a causeway or cobbled road). We used round stones on a roadway, or where we did it, under a bridge to prevent erosion. Though you were down on your knees you had freedom of movement and the foreman left us alone to get on with it. The other job was marking and classifying timber for sale. Classification here was not too intricate; there were three different sized classes. We marked the tree, shouted the classification to the foreman who "booked it down" and that was the basis for sale of the timber. This was the beginning of my ability to measure timber which was later so necessary for me.

Conditions and wages were so much better at Altyre. At Cullen I had ended with 14/- per week. On Altyre estate we had a first-class bothy and a woman who cooked our evening meal, for which we paid extra. We received 17/- a week in wages, plus lodging in the bothy. We worked only five and a half days, with Saturday afternoon off. There were at that time no annual holidays, apart from Christmas Day and New Year's Day. Altyre gave me the foundation of a forestry career, unlike Cullen, where there was no basic training at all.

Chapter 4

The Royal Botanic Gardens and the Glasgow Parks

DURING THE THREE YEARS I SPENT on Cullen and Altyre estates I had been itching for some better training for my career. I was ambitious: I didn't want to stick in the mud all my life, but even with the better training at Altyre I was getting nowhere. Then suddenly out of the blue I heard of a training course for gardeners and foresters in the Royal Botanic Gardens in Edinburgh. The Gardens had been maintained entirely by gardeners, but about the turn of the century the Regius Keeper of the time set up a new scheme for in-depth training. At that time there was no degree in Forestry, only in Agriculture, which covered both subjects. Later on, three Universities – Aberdeen, Glasgow and Edinburgh – gave degrees in Forestry. The Regius Keeper at that time arranged for not merely the thirty or so gardeners but a limited number of foresters to train at evening classes in subjects useful for both gardening and forestry: chemistry, a certain amount of rather elementary physics, in which I had as much knowledge as was required from my schooling in the Albert Road Academy, botany, land surveying and, a subject new to me, geology. I was very keen on geology because it is, to my mind, the foundation of technical and scientific education in forestry and gardening. I heard of this course when I was at Altyre, and I applied immediately to get into the Botanic Gardens. Before admission you had to have a background of three years practical work in forestry or gardening.

I had done my three years, and was accepted, beginning work in January 1908. The first course I remember was surveying, very important for a forester, and in the examination I was surprised and proud to find that I had taken third place. There were two foresters above me, John Murray, an

31

extremely able and clever man, and David Stewart, also able, both slightly older than me, and who had been in the Botanic Gardens a couple of years before me. The chemistry we were taught was very elementary, with a demonstration by the lecturer but no laboratory work at all. I had far more laboratory work at school, which helped a bit. Botany in its various aspects was covered more deeply, but it was a gardeners' course rather than a foresters'. The lecturer placed great stress on the identification of trees, and this was helpful in the long term. In that first year I wasn't satisfied with the evening classes at the Botanic Gardens. I took an evening class at the East of Scotland Agricultural College in Edinburgh, an evening class in forestry which went much deeper than anything we got in the Botanics. That was my first year. In the second year there was the follow-up to the earlier classes. Geology was taught in the second year by a lecturer from Edinburgh University and he treated his subject seriously and deeply. It was one of the subjects I got most out of in the Botanics and I enjoyed it very much. I still wasn't satisfied with one evening class. I went to the Heriot-Watt College and took two subjects apparently not connected with my business but quite necessary: English and Mathematics. This meant that I was doing two nights a week in the Botanics and two at Heriot-Watt, besides working all day.

I was also deeply concerned with religion. I had some close friends in Edinburgh, a family of working people in Leith who were very kind to me. One evening in a discussion about the centre of Edinburgh the word "Cowgate" was mentioned and I was warned not to go near the Cowgate at any price. Whether or not I took this as a challenge I don't know, but I did go down the Cowgate. There, at the foot of the steps in a street which goes up into Chambers Street, I found a band of Christians who were doing what they could to counter the degradation of Cowgate, which remains in my mind as something unbelievable. I went there Saturday after Saturday, taking part in the hymn singing, though I did not do any public speaking. I was able to help draw people, helpless people, utterly degraded, from the pubs which were all over the place. Somehow or other I contracted whooping cough. I must have had it very badly. I was twenty-one at the time, not a youngster, and I had to go back home, the first time I had been back in years. I stayed there some weeks, but the people in Edinburgh seemed to get tired of me being away, and I went back before I should have. The result was a bout of jaundice, and I became a very sick man.

At the beginning of my time at the Botanics I got on very well with the people in charge, especially with the foreman over the foresters, who was a forester himself. In the Botanic Gardens the foresters did all the outside work – the trees, grass-cutting, shrubs, etc. The gardeners kept strictly to the glasshouses, the herbaceous borders and the rock gardens, though we foresters helped in the building of the rock garden as it is now – one of the best rock gardens in the world. The foresters were the only ones who could handle those tons of stone, stones of three or four tons weight. The foresters had nothing to do with the structure or layout of the rock garden, all they had to do was place the stones as required by the experts. The foreman who was quite friendly with me in the beginning seemed to take a "pick" at me and I was sent to do all the labouring jobs, so between me not feeling well and disgust at the work the foreman gave me, I left the Botanics and went home. I had been there just two years. I couldn't finish the three-year course which was required for the certificate. All I got was a testimonial from the Head Gardener, and that ended my period in the Botanic Gardens. I look back on that period as one of the bright patches in my early life, even with all the difficulties and upsets which came to me through illness.

I was at home for several months before I recovered, but recover I did, under the care of my mother. Then I had to look for more work, and I didn't know what. At that time my career was to be forestry, but where I was to go I did not know. However, a friend of ours was a forester in the Glasgow Parks – a young man whom I liked very much indeed – and he was leaving to go abroad. He informed us of this vacancy which was coming up and I applied for, and was appointed to, a job in the Glasgow Parks. I went there in 1908, perhaps in summer or in early autumn. It was very different from the Botanics. They were all young men there, no old men at all except the odd foreman. The make-up of the squads in the Queen's Park was quite different. As far as I remember, I was the only young man in the whole batch. Most of them were ex-gardeners. Some were broken-down men, one or two of whom had been in good service but had just been careless or were pushed out. They then got a job with Glasgow Parks. My job was as a forester, rather different from all the others. I had to look after the trees, and my main job during these two years in Glasgow was pruning dead branches off trees to make them safe for the public. It was a biggish job, and one for a monkey, for I had to climb up all sorts of trees and get down through dangerous branches. Apart from this I had to do a certain amount of grass cutting in the summer time. There again I took evening classes. I went to the Agricultural College, as I was determined to extend the scientific and technical side of my education. In the Agricultural College at that time was one of the most important men in forestry in Britain, Dr Nisbet, who lectured to both day and evening students. I attended his lectures for six months.

At this time I was in close touch with my old friend, Willie McArthur. His father was a strong church worker, and a teetotaller, and Willie and I, both very religious, took up work in Kinning Park where, as I have said, the buildings had originally been set up for a good class of working men but had been degraded by the invasion of Irish and Highlanders. There was a mission church there which Willie and I joined, and we became so concerned that we more or less gave up the idea of doing anything else. Willie did, in the end, decide to go into the ministry and began two years' training for entrance to the University of Glasgow. He ultimately went to the University and started his divinity course. I thought of the same thing. I tried to get into the University but failed, and had to carry on in the Queen's Park. I had come to the stage when I had to make up my mind what I was going to do.

By this time I could have been back on private estates. There was no such thing as state forestry at that time; the Forestry Commission didn't come until many years later. I was offered one or two posts, one a particularly good job through a friend of my father's who was a factor in Doune Estate in Perthshire. I was offered the job of head forester on an estate, but I had come to the stage when nothing would induce me to go back into private estate work as a head forester or almost anything else. Perhaps I should have carried on training in town parks like Glasgow. But the park business was not looked on as an industry, as forestry or gardening were; there was nothing specialised in it. It was in its infancy, and the Glasgow parks gave the lead, in fact. Hatton, who was the head man there, was very able and I think that if I had made my mind to go into that line of business I would have made headway. However, it didn't enter my mind: forestry was my goal. Perhaps it was foolish, because my next eight or ten years were pretty terrible.

Chapter 5

The Years of the First World War

THE ONLY OTHER ASPECT OF FORESTRY was the processing side, and that was where I worked for the next eight years. My brother and I made up our minds to take up work in the home timber trade, but we didn't know what we were in for. There was no difficulty in getting work. Our first job was tree felling for an Ayrshire firm in our own home district. Between 1910 and 1912 there had been one wind blow after another in the countryside and the MacLachlan estate had suffered, like many others. The blown timber was sold to this timber merchant from Ayrshire. We were the felling contractors, working on piece rates, which were scandalously low. We were perhaps at the time not very well trained. I had had six months after my bout of whooping cough and three or four months with a contractor on the Castle Lachlan woodlands. The top-grade timber fellers at the time came from the north of Scotland, Banff, Moray and Aberdeenshire, and the three months' experience with the experts certainly helped me when I set up with my brother. Blown timber, however, is a very different proposition from standing timber, much more difficult, and the rates of pay were not commensurate with the extra work involved. We had a terrible struggle to make a living.

When that job was finished we had to look for another contract. The Ayrshire firm offered us another contract up Loch Awe-side, but the rates were unacceptable, and we were out of a job, but not for long, there was a big demand for fellers at that time, because of the extent of the blown timber. We got a job with a Perthshire firm, William Rattray, a skinflint if ever there was one. However, we were able to get work in Stirlingshire, at Drymen, on the Duke of Montrose's estate, where there were acres and acres of blown timber. Rattray had one of the many sawmills there, and we were given the contract for clear-felling, blown timber again. One contract was for clear-felling medium-sized timber at a certain price per tree for clear-felling, snedding, cross-cutting and clearing certain sections of those trees over a certain diameter. We were fighting for 7d a tree, but all we could get was 6d. It was sheer slavery, and after a year or two I said to Willie: "I am not having this slavery any more. You can please yourself, but I'm giving it up."

We did finally give it up after another contract with a Stirlingshire timber merchant, a man in Drymen, who had a big contract near Plean. The timber was quite near the coal pits there, and we moved to Bannockburn, where we got a house. The contract price was no better, the merchants were all tarred with the same stick. By this time I had to make a living for two of us, as I had married.

When I was working in the Glasgow Parks, I went with Willie McArthur to a mission church, where we both fell in love with two of the young church workers. Willie married first. He had had to give up his work for the ministry, and was in the assaying business, working in iron and steel for Colvilles, and making a living there, though not a very profitable one. I married Belle Thomson, of whom more later, before I left the home timber trade. We set up house, first in a small house, just one room and a kitchen, but when we got the contract near Plean we flitted to a house in Bannockburn. Willie (my brother) had an adjoining house in what was termed a garden city. After moving we began work on the contract, which was for felling very big oaks, an extremely hard job and one we had little experience of. I had only seen this type of work at Cullen, when they were felling big old beech and oak trees of blown timber. We found life very difficult. In addition, Belle and I had to clean up our cottage, as we had followed a miner's family who had not been so careful. Willie and I worked in winter from 7 in the morning to 5 at night, sometimes quite in the dark, to enable us to make a living at all.

At the end of this we decided to have no more contract work. I had made up my mind to try for the management side of the home timber trade, and we both applied to a big Stirlingshire firm, Jones of Larbert, one of the most noted firms in Scottish home timber processing. They were delighted to take us on, as they had found it difficult to get steady men they could rely on to manage this work in what they called temporary sawmills all over Scotland. Willie was appointed first, to Clackmannanshire, in charge of clear-felling and sawmilling there. He got on so well with Jones of Larbert that he remained with them for the rest of his working life. When he had finished the job in Clackmannan, he went to Aberdeenshire and established himself there as one of the best managers

Jones had for this kind of work. He was pensioned off by then, and died in Huntly not so very long ago.

My experience with Jones was very different from his. I found them skinflints and eventually I left them. Before that, after we settled in Bannockburn I went to evening classes in Stirling in chemistry and physics, so that when Jones offered me a job that would have taken me away from the district, I refused. However, he accommodated me, and offered me a job with a sawmill in Larbert, six miles from Bannockburn and I accepted. I had to be at the sawmill at 7.30 in the morning, and worked till 5 at night, cycling the six or seven miles morning and night. After a bite of food I went two nights a week to the High School in Stirling to my evening classes. I found the teachers very able and sympathetic. In the sawmill I also got the training I wanted. It was hard work, and poorly paid, and meant a long day, which must have been very hard on Belle as a new wife in that cottage. Perhaps I asked too much of her. In any case I carried on till the spring of 1909 when Jones offered me a job as outside foreman, the title given to those in management, probably to keep our wages as low as possible, as we weren't foremen, we were actually managers.

Up to that time I had been working in the sawmill, tailing, that is, I was the second man to a trained sawyer on the long bench, as it was called, handling very big timber. Other benches, the so-called breast benches, handled smaller timber, for mining, etc., but the one bench of vital importance I thought at the time was this huge bench where we handled great logs of timber.

Being a tailsman meant assisting the expert, and he had to be expert, sawing as he did extremely valuable huge logs of oak or beech, he had to know exactly what he was doing to get every cubic foot of sawn timber out of the log. The main practical job of the tailsman was to go down into the pit where the sawdust landed, clear it out and barrow it away to the sawdust pit.

Sawmilling is a dangerous job when the saws are fully protected and it is sad to relate that Jones of Larbert had not fully protected their breast benches. I saw one man on a breast bench killed when the log got locked on to the saw, was carried over the top of the saw and like a bullet hit the sawyer. Just after that accident I inspected foreign timber saws which were protected, so that the saw could not carry a jammed log. Towards the end of my time in the sawmill I was put on to grading pit props which were being cut at the benches. However, the time came for a change and I took a job I was offered in Perthshire, managing blown and standing timber in Lansdowne's estate at Meikleour near Blairgowrie.

We got a small cottage, now scrapped, which was derelict even then, but we were glad to get into something which would keep the two of us together and house the small amount of furniture we had. I was in charge of an outside sawmill, as it was called, similar to the long bench I had worked on at Larbert. In this case we were sawing one species, Scots Pine, but larger, quite mature Scots Pine, which had to be carefully handled. We also carried out clear-felling of timber for use in the mines. The supply of round pit props was, until the war, entirely in the hands of foreign importers, the home timber trade never tackled that aspect of the work. In 1914 supplies had to be got from other sources, as there was no importation of timber during the war. One source I was asked to handle was coppice oak, i.e. oak grown from stumps, two or three stems to a stump. Foreign props had been beautiful timber: clean, peeled, straight and light, just what miners working under cramped conditions needed. What we were sending to the pits was a downright scandal – heavy oak, rough barked, not always quite straight, it must have been a nightmare for the miners to handle that stuff.

The whole outfit was a miserable affair. The engine was most uncertain, only kept going by the efforts of a clever old engineer, and it was impossible to manage it with any hope of success. I came to an end of my efforts to handle the business. I was receiving £200 a year at the time, poor pay, and I asked for another £100 a year. They didn't give me £300, they gave me £250, and that just about finished it for me. An advertisement appeared in the press for a manager in a home timber business, and I applied, but received a reply that they had appointed someone else. Shortly after, they wrote to ask if I would take on a job as second in hand under an undermanager in their headquarters at Grangemouth. The pay was about £500, twice as much as I was getting from Jones as undermanager, and I left and went to Grangemouth.

This job was almost as bad as when I was managing on my own. The manager in Grangemouth was almost an alcoholic, and it was one of those foreign timber mining supply sawmills which had had to go over to home timber, in the handling of which they had no experience at all. I was given no responsibility and the manager hated having me there. A few months later I was asked to take over control of the sawmill and woodland felling on Skene estate in Aberdeenshire, which I had applied for previously. I accepted and took charge of this unit which was preparing entirely home grown timber props. I found the unit in a chaotic state. The man who had been appointed knew nothing about the home timber trade, and I had to redd up his affairs. He had gone on cutting props, but had piled them up in one stack after another, ungraded, and it took me weeks to get them classified, a job at which I was by this time something of an expert. They were in all sizes, from six feet long to about two feet, and they had to be separated and classified. I didn't do any sawing till this was finished, and then we started to saw, classifying them as we went. Within a few weeks we were despatching perhaps five or six wagons a day, practically the whole of our sawn timber was despatched. Our headquarters in Glasgow were so overjoyed they gave me a bonus of £50 in my next pay. When that sawmill finished, we had to buy up timber in other places, and we went finally to a very big proposition in Lumsden where the timber was bought with my help as valuer. My figures were agreed, and I was left to handle the sawmilling. But the end of the war came and the trade fell quite flat. I was kept on by the firm, but there was no business at all, and I just didn't know what to do.

In 1919, however, my career in the home timber trade ended, because I applied to the Forestry Commission for a position as a forester with them. The Commission was set up in 1919, and I was appointed to take charge of a forest in Morayshire. This was what I had wanted all my life, to establish plantations for the future, and now I had got it.

"Ye see yon birkie ca'd, a lord,
Wha struts, and stares, and a' that,
Though hundreds worship at his word,
He's but a coof, for a' that."

Robert Burns

"Song — For A' That And A' That"

"To secure for the workers by hand or by brain the full fruits of their industry and the most equitable distribution thereof that may be possible upon the basis of the common ownership of the means of production, distribution and exchange and the best obtainable system of popular administration and control of each industry or service."

Section 4 Clause 4 of the Labour Party Constitution and Standing Orders

From *Who Owns Scotland?*

Chapter 6

With the Forestry Commission

1919 to 1928

JUST BEFORE THE END OF THE WAR a man Ackland was asked to report on the future of forestry. During the war private enterprise had been unable to satisfy the demand for timber, and the Coalition Government of 1918 determined to ensure that in an emergency there would be adequate supplies of timber, so the Forestry Commission was set up. Lord Lovat was appointed Chairman, a private landowner who owned extensive tracts of land in Scotland. He was Chairman for several years and organised four divisions in Scotland – Aberdeen, Inverness, Glasgow and Edinburgh – but at a very early period the Glasgow one was disbanded. The four Divisions were under Divisional Officers, and we in Scotland were extremely fortunate in the men who were appointed to the top of three of the Divisions. One was an unfortunate choice but the other three were men who had risen from the ranks, able men who had proved what they could do in private enterprise. Each Divisional Officer had three assistants, called Junior Divisional Officers. Below them came the foresters, grades 1 and 2. These were the only people who were graded and could become permanent Civil Servants. Below them were the foremen, gangers and workmen. That was the set-up in the whole of Britain.

I later came to know one of the Scottish Divisional Officers intimately. Frank Scott had been at one time a forester with the Earl of Mansfield in Scone Palace. During the war he had had an important job arranging and planning supplies of timber on the continent. He was the man appointed in Aberdeen, a very able man. The other appointee was Anand, who had a similar background to Scott, had been a head forester for a long time but had given it up and lectured in a college in Durham. He also had a background of private enterprise, and had taken the Botanic Gardens course. The Glasgow man was Wilkinson, whose father had been a piano maker in Forres, and he was extremely keen to make a career in forestry, but that Division was blotted out within a short period of time, to save money. The fourth man was John Murray in Edinburgh. He and I had been mates in the Botanic Gardens and I knew him quite well. We should have been close friends, but somehow or other our outlooks were not the same: he was tied up hand and foot with the private estates, and by this time I had no time for them at all. Anand knew my views, but he and I became very close.

The objective of each Division was to do what they could to establish forests: to find land for acquisition by the Forestry Commission, to set up a state enterprise in timber. Frank Scott became very busy, because he didn't know the north-west, where he was placed, at all, but he was able and a pusher, and acquired considerable acres of land for the Forestry Commission in its first season, 1919 to 1920. The first Report was published in 1920, and in this year Frank Scott had acquired five or six estates with considerable acres, planted up with timber. I don't think Murray managed to get any land in the south, and none in the east, not surprising, because the east is tighter in regard to releasing land. There was more land to be released in the crofting counties of the north-west where Scott was. Anand got going in the second year, and secured land owned at one time by the Duke of Fife in Morayshire. He owned over 200,000 acres – perhaps as much as 250,000 or 260,000 – in the north of Scotland, in Banff and Moray. The batch of land acquired by Anand was about half-way between Elgin and Forres, about 3000 acres, I think, and I was appointed forester.

Anand, Scott and I all had the Botanic Gardens background, while they also had experience of working on private estates. I did not have the backing of any of the private landowners. Anand and Scott also had a first-class certificate in Forestry granted by the Highland and Agricultural Society, which demanded a considerable amount of knowledge, and was said to be equal to an ordinary degree in Forestry or Agriculture. I had been studying for years for it, but hadn't been able to settle down sufficiently to sit for the degree, but later when I was settled in Monaughty I took up the work for the degree, and, after an examination lasting three days, I obtained it in 1922, two years after I was appointed. It had meant a lot of hard work to be able to get there, and it wasn't everybody who could get it. I believe Anand and Scott got it in one shot, as I did: I was very proud of that. One of the District Officers who was over me had three shots at it before he got it but he was in front of me. John Murray and I were at the Botanic Gardens together. He was probably more able than any of us, went to University and took a B.Sc. in Forestry. I was only appointed as a Grade 1 forester. With my background I suppose they knew quite well where I stood regarding ownership and regarded me as a rebel. However, I was appointed there, beginning at the end of September or beginning of October 1920. I was told I had to get 500 acres planted up that year from scratch – there was not a man nor a tool in the place, and others, e.g. in Inverness, had never been asked to plant more than 100 acres. I told Anand I thought it impossible, but the figure had been settled in headquarters in Edinburgh. So I had to go ahead and get together men and tools to plant up 500 acres. People perhaps didn't realise what a big job it was. The land had fairly recently, during the war, been cleared of timber, but in the rush of war nothing was done with the hag, the branch wood from the felled timber, which covered the whole area. Furthermore, there was draining to be done. I did not think that fencing was necessary, and in the first period, less than a year, we planted one face of the hill without fencing. To keep down the rabbits and hares I appointed a trapper. My first trapper was a man who was the most noted poacher in Morayshire – or even in the north of Scotland. I am not sure if I knew that at the time, but I did know that he was <u>the</u> man to clear out the rabbits. With snares, traps and guns he cleared out every rabbit on that exposed northern side of the hill, facing on to the Moray Firth. This hill was called Heldon Hill, the Burghead water supply came from it, but the Forestry Commission called the estate Monaughty, which was the name of a big farm on the estate which had nothing to do with the forestry side. It should have been called Heldon Hill.

That is by the way. I had to make a list of tools, which came quite quickly, and get the men together, not difficult in 1920 when unemployment was severe. We cleared and drained the land and planted it up in rectangular sections of 50 acres, one after the other. In the second year we had to plant 600 acres, and in roughly the centre of this I left four 30-acre "compartments" unplanted, and built a rusky of rough branches big enough for 30 or 40 men. When the men came out on a stormy day I hated to send them back, as they had often come a fairly long distance to their work, so they could shelter when necessary in the hut, and get part of a day's wages. The men appreciated this, as they were able to have a whole week's wages instead of broken time.

I worked a squad of thirty or forty people, usually divided into two squads, under a foreman, and a draining squad of three or four under a sub-foreman. After clearing the hag and draining, we started on the tricky operation, planting. On the Altyre estate we had to get in 1000 plants per day, and this was the figure the Forestry Commission had aimed at on the west coast. My aim was nothing like this. I wanted to do a first-class job in placing the plants carefully in the soil to give them the chance of getting a root hold, so that when the growing season came they could take off. My figure was 650 per man per day, and I had no difficulty in attaining that figure. At that time planting was done with the ordinary garden spade, but I made sure that ours were of good quality, and not the great clubby things I had to use in my early training. Ultimately I obtained No.2 Skelton spades, which were beautifully made and a joy to handle.

The plants were supplied in the first year from all over the country, from Aberdeen and other places in Scotland, but the great bulk from the south of England, Old Norway Spruce which was all that could be got at that time, as nursery work was just beginning. The plants were not up to my standards, they were just acceptable, and we had to use them. They came in truckloads from the south of England, in closed vans, and were taken from the station, and dumped just beside the shed we used as a starting point in the morning.

Norway Spruce was a European species in use in Britain for many years; the sitka spruce was not so well known at that time. If I were planting today there would be a big difference in this selection. I would use practically no larch, which was one of the main species used at that time. It would have been much easier to lay out the ground, as the great bulk would have been in sitka spruce. Scots Pine too would not have been planted so generously as it was at that time. We were fortunate in that the first season was a particularly good one, and though I had thought it impossible to plant 500 acres, we planted just over that by the end of the season.

On the domestic side, we were housed. My wife and I were given a sad, sad, sad affair, a most brutish ugly hut plus a bothy which had been erected to enable a batch of men, ten or twelve, to live there, with separate cubicles for the beds, and cooking equipment. This saved them the long journey of six or seven miles on a bicycle. We had a 60 x 20 foot corrugated iron hut. I arrived there in October, when the hut had just been transported from the north of Scotland, a war-time hut made entirely of corrugated iron. It was ready for my wife and me to go into at the end of the year. Belle was in Lumsden all this time, and I was in lodgings in Elgin, coming out every morning on my bicycle.

The hut was a dreadful affair. That corner was one of the windiest I have ever experienced, the wind rattled the hut almost like a drum, constantly. The rain rattled on it too, but the wind was the biggest problem. It was not watertight, wind and snow came through into the rooms, and I had to stop up the gaps between the sections with paper to keep the water from being blown into the rooms. I kept it dry but the sound of the wind was there all the time. The hut comprised a bathroom with hot and cold water, a fairly big kitchen which was probably meant to be used as a sitting room, and two bedrooms. The partitions dividing the rooms and the lining of the hut was asbestos, the partitions were new asbestos, but on the walls were sheets which had been used when the army occupied the hut and they were plastered over with some sort of paper and the rest of it. No attempt was made at redecorating the hut, but finally they sent up two pots of colour, I think one was red and the other green, to cover up the bare grey asbestos as well as the annoying display on the other sections. The Forestry Commission didn't care what happened to the people they were employing. My wife came to live there at Christmas time, and she was in that hut before any decorating was done. We couldn't settle; it had a bad effect on my wife which really affected all the remaining part of her life. I complained to the responsible department of the Forestry Commission, and some of them came along to see it. Their response to my complaints was to say: "Now, come on, look at the buildings the farm servants have to work in." Some of the houses may have been pretty derelict, but they were, unlike ours, on the whole wind and water proof. Our house was typical of Forestry Commission houses in the west of Scotland. No-one complained to the extent that I did, but I didn't get very far, two pots of paint at the end of the planting season.

One of our big problems was bracken cutting. The bracken ground was usually planted in larch, which were light-demanding trees, not like the sitka or Norway spruce which were shade-bearing trees. These are the two distinguishing features of the trees which are planted in forestry. The Scots Pine comes midway between the larch and the spruces. The larch could not stand any shade at all, so we had to do something about cutting down the bracken. For this I devised a tool with which the men could cut down acres of bracken in a day.

I had cleared out the rabbits on the north side, but we had an invasion from the south side. There were rabbits on practically every estate in Britain. Though they are not game, they are considered desirable in training people in blood sports, in shooting the grouse, pheasants, deer, etc. Soon after my first year, the south side was taken over by the Forestry Commission, still with thousands of rabbits on it. It was a much smaller area than the north side, but more valuable, being more fertile and able to carry extremely heavy crops, in the long term, such as sitka spruce and Douglas Fir. When I mentioned to the gamekeeper that we would have to clear out the rabbits he said, "You will never clear them out of this ground, never, you needn't try." However, I got Willie Mathieson (the poacher/trapper) on to it, during the summer when he wouldn't be engaged in planting. I gave him a completely free hand, and probably six months to finish the work, but he cleared out the rabbits completely in three or four, not a rabbit was left on the whole estate. After that we were able to plant up without fencing, and I never saw any trace of rabbit damage at that time. The estates loved the rabbit, the Forestry Commission under my charge hated them.

The beginning made in my first year in Monaughty made it easier to carry on in the second year an extra programme of 600 acres. In spite of the hateful conditions under which we lived I had established a routine, part of which was to go each Friday evening to Elgin five miles away to collect the cash for paying the wages. The main routine work was of course overseeing the planting programme, which was very tiring, allowing little leisure or freedom at any time.

We were still very discontented with the house, and I complained continuously, until we got to the stage when I threatened to leave. I would have regretted it, but it was impossible for a man with a wife to live in these conditions. At the beginning of 1924, however, the Forestry Commission acquired a new forest at Teindland, from the estates of the Duke of Richmond and Gordon, south of Elgin in the Fochabers district. We moved there in 1925, to one of the most comfortable little houses I have ever been in. It was a wooden house. Jones of Larbert was trying to get a market for houses built of home timber, and this was a sample one. The only drawback was that there was no bathroom, which we had had in our house in Monaughty. There was no inside water supply, and there was an outside earth closet. Apart from this the house and its situation were perfect. It consisted of two bedrooms and a kitchen, but we used one of the bedrooms as a kind of den. The water had to be carried from a small well just outside the garden gate. There was a fair-sized, pleasant garden, with a wooden fence against rabbits.

Though I had transferred to Teindland, I was still in charge of Monaughty, with an under-forester as my deputy. The Forestry Commission also acquired a small estate of a few hundred acres at Ordiequish, belonging to the Seafield property. This was actually over the Spey in Banffshire, but was closely attached to Morayshire, and near the Richmond and Gordon estate. It was taken over in 1927 and developed into a huge forest called Speymouth, of many thousands of acres.

Teindland is particularly interesting because a great deal of research was done on it. Mark L. Anderson who was Research Officer in 1924 when that area was taken over started off his research station on poor land. He left the Commission in 1925 or 1926, but that didn't stop developments. Horse ploughing was begun on the land to be planted. I had done some ploughing on a stretch of land on Ordiequish in the planting programme of 1927. We did not get the depth with horse ploughing that was required to make any vital change, but even this small amount of shallow ploughing made a difference. Dr Pyatt, a soil scientist, had brought out evidence which has revolutionised our ideas of working this type of poor soil. He studied the nature of the soil conditions under the surface, to five, six or even seven feet deep. We all knew that there was an "iron band" under the top spit which was difficult to break, but could be done with fairly deep ploughing. Pyatt didn't finish there. He found that three or four feet down there was another band, not a narrow one like the one we called the iron band but a piece of completely consolidated soil under the subsoil caused by pressure during the Ice Age. Through this neither water nor roots could penetrate. Pyatt's work was revolutionary, because, if deep enough ploughing is carried out, to three or four feet, and this tight band of subsoil is broken up, the water will flow from top to bottom, and roots may even percolate to that depth. I have seen one small area here in Perthshire where that deep ploughing has been carried out, and it seemed to revolutionise the whole business: everything looked a natural field for growing timber.

Pyatt's pioneering work is also important because forestry must not encroach on agricultural land, not even poor grazing. Up to 95% of our plantations had to be placed on land of second or even third grade quality, uplands and even some hill land. Pyatt's work has made it possible to grow economic forests on land we couldn't have used previously, up to seven or eight hundred feet, over eight hundred feet is not viable. It is wonderful to think that the State, not private enterprise, has been 100% responsible for this work.

The plantation at Monaughty which I planted is now sixty-four years of age, [this was in 1984], and it is, under existing ideas of rotation, twenty-four years over what it should be. Teindland is now sixty, and Ordiequish about fifty-seven, but the rest of the Speymouth forest is younger. If I were planting today in Monaughty, I would put 90% of it under sitka spruce, instead of the three or four species we planted then. We would thus be concerned with handling only one species. The other 10% might be used for growing trees which might break up a little what people describe as blank stretches of dark-coloured packed conifer forests. I have no objection to them because I know the value of these forests and the financial returns which are made from these dense acres of dark green. Larch could perhaps be used, Japanese larch grows quite fast and would change the outline, as would birches and some hardwoods, but, in the main, if forestry is going to be a commercial enterprise and communities are going to be formed depending on forestry, on a forest industry, then sitka spruce has to be planted in bulk. Sitka spruce is essential for the development of a British forestry that will be economic and lead to the setting up of new communities.

There is one other aspect of the Forestry Commission which is sad, and that is that it was appointed as a commission and not as a civil service department like the Department of Agriculture. Forestry was taken out of the private landowners' hands because they were considered unfit to do what the Commission has done, but they tried to keep a grip on the Forestry Commission and have done so all along. Lord Lovat was the first Chairman of the Commission – a powerful, domineering character. The life of the Forestry Commission Divisional Officers, Conservators as they are now called, was a pretty miserable one in the early days because he was so domineering. The Divisional Officers had been brought up under private enterprise, and it was no doubt difficult for them to break away, and certainly Lovat took advantage of it. Lovat was there for seven years, and was followed by a series of big landowners, some from Scotland, some from England, until quite recently, I think about 1965, it was broken during the time of the 1964-1970 Labour Government. They decided the Commission should be remodelled and ended the power of the landowners who were no longer appointed Chairmen. The first Chairman after this was a timber merchant who sat for five years and made little change. The next one was a socialist, a Labour man, Lord Taylor of Griff. Tom Taylor he was when I knew him, an important figure in the Cooperative Society in Glasgow, covering the whole of Scotland. I didn't think he made the most of that position, and I had some correspondence with him which may have made some impression. He became second Chairman of the renovated Forestry Commission. The Chairman was not paid a salary, but only an honorarium, small in the beginning, but latterly quite substantial. These non-technical Chairmen were only part-time. The day-to-day work of the Forestry Commission was carried on in the three countries by the Director of Forestry; there was a Director in each of the three countries. Tom Taylor seemed to me to be keener to support private enterprise rather than State forestry. Grants were given to private enterprise, not large, but enough to enable them to do the work, but in spite of them, though the Forestry Commission between 1919 and the Second World War developed a huge planting programme, the planting programme of private enterprise remained negligible compared with the Forestry Commission's. This is proved by the fact that today, more than sixty years after the establishment of the Forestry Commission, the woodlands, particularly in Scotland, developed almost entirely on Forestry Commission plantations. The Government now wants to privatise all the land the Commission has got, and to kill the Forestry Commission entirely. The Tories have all along hated the Forestry Commission, and must have hated them very deeply when they saw the land they had once owned developing into magnificent plantations, which are now proving extremely profitable financially. We are at the stage where the Forestry Commission is on the way out. The planting programme has been cut to just minor areas, and we are once again in the power of the landowning class.

This set-up has always worried me on two counts, political and educational, which are so intertwined in my mind that I cannot keep them separate. On the political side, the career system in the Forestry Commission is tied hand and foot to what I can call the officer class, vis-à-vis the ordinary working forester. This officer class is so limited in its outlook regarding what should be taking place in state forestry that it has been severely restricted during the past sixty-five years, and will remain that way until some drastic changes take place. The political aspect is tied up with the educational. Some education for forestry was given in the Botanic Gardens and later on in the Agricultural Colleges which granted certificates, though this was of very limited value. Three universities at one time offered degrees – Glasgow, Edinburgh and Aberdeen – but Glasgow has now ceased to do so, and only Edinburgh and Aberdeen offer ordinary degrees, honours degrees and doctorates. This helps only those who gain admission to university, which is at present very limited. I should like to see the day come when the great majority of people can go to university, but at present the working people are tied down to a limited education in forestry. This is true of other subjects, but in forestry it is particularly bad. The schools of forestry tried out by the Forestry Commission failed completely, being concerned with basic training in felling, planting, etc. and giving no scientific education at all in chemistry, physics, botany and geology. I have fought for an H.N.D. in forestry which would be on a level with an ordinary degree. This is important for promotion. Only men with a degree could get promotion, yet the working foresters have been responsible for much of the work of the Forestry Commission in the past sixty-five years.

Chapter 7

Changing fortunes: North Wales and Eire, the Depression Years

I FOUND THE SYSTEM OF PROMOTION objectionable, but not so objectionable that I wouldn't face up to promotion, in fact, I fought for it because I wanted some of us who had been kept at the bottom getting on and helping to guide the Forestry Commission as only a field man could do. After eight years as a forester I was promoted in 1928 to District Officer rank. I was transferred to Gwydr in North Wales, one of the most beautiful districts I have ever been in, a delightful countryside to live and work in. I had five forests to take over, scattered all over North Wales. We were promised a house, a glowing description of which was given by the Conservator or Regional Officer, a man named Sanger. The District Officer soon disillusioned me about it: it was scheduled for demolition, being completely dilapidated. It had been described as having an avenue leading to it from Holyhead Road, and as having a glass house attached. We did have a look at it, we didn't just go by the District Officer's description, but we said at once that we couldn't live in it. Our furniture was on the way, but we managed to stop it and put it into storage until we required it.

Another objectionable aspect of forestry housing was in one of the districts, where the forester's house was designed so that the District Officers could live with the forester and his wife at any time he was in that district. I happened to know the forester who had been given the house and staying with him would just not have suited me at all. I was not going to live with a forester with whom I had been working all day. I might have had trouble with him, had an argument with him about various things, and it was just not on to go and live with him in the evening. I met the Regional Officer, Sanger, shortly after I had been told about this practice. I had worked with him before when he was a Research Officer doing a time and motion study on my planting squad. I told him I would not consider for a single minute living in the forester's house. He looked at me and said, "It's all right, we will just notify headquarters that I can't accept you as District Officer." "You can please yourself," I replied – I was certainly not going to toe the line. However, nothing happened, and I worked for three months under him.

In spite of these irritations, I enjoyed my work in Wales. There were a number of plantations of sitka spruce, which was my speciality, all needing some attention. The management after planting had not been very carefully done in any of the forests, and as a working forester promoted to District Officer I was welcomed with open arms by every one of the foresters, especially by the two Scotsmen and the five District Officers. However, this was to be only for three months. They were happy months for me, travelling all over North Wales. I enjoyed the scenery and the countryside. They were not so pleasant for Belle, though we rented a quite pleasant wooden house, not at all isolated, after the summer visitors had gone, in the autumn of 1928.

I had, however, before I was appointed to District Officer, applied for a vacancy in the Irish Free State, as Divisional Officer. After I had been in Gwydr for a couple of months I was told the post was mine if I cared to take it, though if I had been happily settled in Wales I doubt if I would have taken it, so I went to Dublin at the end of 1928. I had been in three positions in 1928 – as forester with the Forestry Commission, as District Officer with the Commission and as Higher Executive Officer in the Forestry Section of the Department of Agriculture in the Irish Free State, as it then was, in Dublin. A completely and totally new way of life for me!

I was given one month in the office to get my bearings, as we had vast areas under our charge. I use the word vast because they stretched from Donegal to Cork, twenty-six or twenty-seven forests scattered from the north to the south. After that month I had got my bearings and then I was out in the field. I also had to do a certain amount of office work, but I soon discovered it was the field work that really required my attention. I found chaos everywhere. I couldn't visit all the forests at once, in fact, I was there for rather over a couple of years and at the end of the day there were one or two forests which I never inspected.

During this time there was a concept among the private forestry people I changed when I was with the Forestry Commission: the notion that you had to have a death rate in any new planting. I thought this was stark staring mad. A death rate of 40%-70% might often be found, and nobody thought anything of a 10, 15 or 20% death rate in a new planting. My objective was 100% growth without death rate at all, and I frequently got that, but anything over 10% was no use to me.

I also had to organise the nursery end of the growing. When I arrived in Ireland the method was to get samples of plants from England and Scotland, particularly from Scotland, as they didn't grow their own plants in Ireland. We selected the best varieties and prices from these samples, and placed orders for tens of thousands of plants, big orders, because planting was going full out in Ireland with its twenty-seven forests. Most of our plants came from Scotland, where climate and conditions were similar, and I knew the Scots nurserymen very well and knew where the best plants could be got. The plants we bought in were lined out in the nurseries attached to each forest. In Scotland the Forestry Commission had its own distributing nurseries, and grew their own, and it paid dividends.

I enjoyed the period in Ireland and meeting the men. I was in the office often enough, but I was a good deal in the field because that was where I felt it was necessary for me to be. Later on, when the work settled down, there would not have been the same necessity for one to come out of the office, and I could have had a much easier life, as I would have depended on these men. I look back on it as an extremely happy period in my life.

I was also thrown into other important work in the acquisition of land for our forestry programmes. My first experience of this was Crozier, on an estate in Donegal. It took us a day and a half to get there by train from Dublin to Donegal, across the border into Ulster. We had to put up for a night at Strabane, and then move on next morning into Donegal by train, getting up at about six in the morning.

On the question of acquisition: I had several to deal with which were comparatively easy. There was never timber to be valued – it was always land and that was fairly straightforward; there was never any difficulty about a final figure. However, one piece of trouble I did have – rather an amusing one. I was asked to go and inspect land offered by the Church in the south of the country. I am afraid I disappointed the clerics very much. I was given a lunch in their house and treated in a way I probably never was before or since. The table was crammed with everything, every conceivable quality of booze, as much as I would like to drink, and top grade food. I had a good meal, but no drinks. I don't know if they were disappointed or not – I could have been filled fou' but I wasn't. There were three clerics there, one of whom went with me to interview the people who were offering the land and to show me where the land was. I met the people, they were quite ordinary, decent peasants. One was Protestant, and I seem to have spoken with him alone. He inferred that he would not be there very long, as Catholicism had increased since Ireland became an independent country. However, that was none of my business, I never saw any sign of it when I was moving among the Roman Catholic workers and others. In this case, I got under the priests' skin: I would not look at the land they were offering, and recommended it should not be purchased. My advice was taken and the land was not bought for forestry.

As regards our domestic life in Ireland, for six or seven months we rented a not very suitable house in a west central suburb of Dublin. Then we got a house in Strathmines, the most pleasant part of Dublin for living in. Yet my wife never seemed happy in Ireland and in 1930 she became seriously ill, and broke down completely. We were advised by doctors we called in that it would be better if we didn't stay in Ireland. It came as a shock to me because I thought I would be settled there for life, but in the end I just made up my mind that I couldn't sacrifice my wife for a career. We gave up the house, and flitted around April or thereby of 1931. And that was the end of my career in Ireland.

Looking back over my period in Ireland I feel I attained some results. One of my successes there was a change in the supply of plants which had come entirely from Scotland. Before I left we bought seed as well as plants and the seed was immediately sown into the nursery beds. In one or two years they would be able to supply all the demand for plants in the Irish Free State. That was one of the things I was happy to see changing so completely while I was there.

Another success was at the huge annual agricultural show in the suburbs of Dublin. We were advertising our aspect of land use in Ireland and we tried to create a feeling of kinship with agriculture. In the past, even in Scotland, and in Britain, there had always been a feeling of opposition between agriculture and forestry and we tried to break that down in Ireland.

I had been in the Irish Free State for two and a half years and I regretted having to leave. However, I had to get packed up, and took the boat from Dublin to Glasgow. I had the furniture to take, plus a dog and a small car which I had used considerably in Ireland – all of which meant money. Belle was still quite ill, and I had to take care of her. I went for a very short period of time to my folks in Rutherglen, but I didn't want to be a burden on them for any length of time. I had no work and I planned to take a couple of rooms in a pleasant corner in the outskirts of Dunoon on the Clyde. I don't remember how long we lived there, perhaps a couple of months, and I was trying to get work of some sort. Work was not easily available in 1931. There was a Depression. The Labour Government was still in power and I didn't know much about their affairs, having been out of the country for a couple of years. I didn't approach the Forestry

Commission, though some people advised me to do so. The Assistant Commissioner himself asked me to come and have an interview with him, but it wasn't with the intention of offering me work which I could accept. In any case I went and saw him and discussed the matter with him.

What I wanted was work in the field as an ordinary worker, plus a smallholding. That was the practice on a great many units which the Forestry Commission had acquired. I wanted a wage coming in weekly which would be sufficient to keep us alive while I was building up a nursery stock. I always had a notion for growing alpines and rock plants and dwarf shrubs, and I didn't want to go back to the Commission as a graded forester. The Assistant Commissioner did offer me something of that kind but I told him quite bluntly that I wasn't going to start at the bottom again and climb, and I was unemployed for a period of about nine months.

Finally I wrote to Tom Johnston, who was in the Scottish Office in the Labour Government. I told him the circumstances, that I was unemployed with no government payment coming in, I hadn't the necessary stamps to entitle me to unemployment benefit. He must have gone to the Forestry Commission direct, as Secretary of State for Scotland, and ultimately I was offered a job in Argyllshire, on Lochawe, as a draining contractor. I didn't get the job with the smallholding that I wanted, but I had to accept this. It was the first time I had to make a living out of draining. I had had seven or eight years of making a living out of felling trees and preparing them for the sawmills, on contract, but it was not easy to get into the way of making a living out of draining at so much per chain. I had to buy my own tools, and I employed a very capable man, going canny in the beginning because I hadn't the money to pay wages. He had done all kinds of work on the land, though he hadn't done much draining, and between the two of us we became quite expert. I had been used to handling hand tools, but not the big Rutters we had to use opening drains.

There were always two of us who were non-Gaelic speakers, and three or four who were all Gaelic speakers. I built up a first-class squad. I was responsible for the work, I was a capitalist on a small scale, being responsible for supplying tools, insurance, etc., but within six or eight months I was able to get sufficient chainage to enable me to pay the wages and other outlays and make some profit. The contract lasted the best part of two years, then it came to an end, the men had to be paid off, and I was on my beam end again. I thought the Commission had practically guaranteed me work, but that wasn't the case.

When my contract finished in Kilchrenan I had to think of going away to find work somewhere else, but in the meantime Belle and I arranged to use our house for bed and breakfast visitors. It was quite a popular district for visitors, particularly in the summer, and though we weren't rushed, we always had a certain amount of cash coming in. That was our only income. I had set up a nursery to grow alpines and small shrubs, heathers and rhododendrons, and made a big sowing of a variety of plants which would be of use later for sale. I specialised in primulas and Himalayan rhododendrons. However, the day came when some change had to take place. We saw an advertisement for a nursery in Stirlingshire with glass on it, about two acres of land plus a fairly extensive area of glass, to rent. We got into correspondence with the owners and finally rented the nursery and flitted there.

The new work I was attempting in Campsie Glen was one of the biggest challenges I think I have ever had. If I had been a gardener, trained in the Botanic Gardens as a gardener instead of a forester, it would have been right up my street. But I had no experience of glass work. I had to start from scratch, which at my age and with my background was a challenge. I had to accept it and make the most of it. I had always been accustomed to hard work, and this meant very hard work. When the tomatoes were on the go you had to be there at 5 or 6 o'clock in the morning to make sure your heat was correct, and to get your furnaces cleaned up and fired up again, and from then on it was work up to 5 or 6 o'clock at night – no release, no relief, no time off. I found it extremely hard, but it wouldn't have mattered so much if the market had been sufficiently lively to enable me to get reasonable prices for the material I was growing, but the market at that time seemed to be at rock bottom. I never attempted selling my tomatoes in the market because the market price was quite impossible for me as an amateur grower.

The war began and we had bombs all round us in the serious Clydebank bombing which caused so much damage and death. I don't know if this had any effect or not, but in the end I just gave up the nursery business entirely. In the interval I had been fortunate enough to get a piece of land in Bearsden to rent. Earlier on it would have been a godsend, and might have been a godsend in the long term as well. We flitted everything we had to Bearsden. Houses were impossible, but we were able to get a shop which was for let, and convert it into reasonable living conditions. However, I found it impossible to make a living in that line. I gave it all up and went back to my old line, forestry and timber manufacture. I joined the Homegrown Timber Supply Department of the Board of Trade, closed up everything in Milngavie and Bearsden, and went to Morayshire, to Grantown-on-Spey to tackle the work there.

Chapter 8

The Second World War
and the Post-War Years

THE SECOND WORLD WAR PUT AN end to my efforts to make a living in the nursery trade, particularly as I was concerned more with ornamental gardening. I felt I needed to do something more to pull my weight in the war effort. I knew about the Board of Trade and its branch, the Home Timber Supply Department, set up to cover the manufacture of timber for war purposes. I don't know why a government department was set up, they must have been dissatisfied with the amount of timber being produced by private enterprise but the same thing had happened in the First World War. About six or seven divisions of this Homegrown Timber Supply Department were set up all over Scotland and I approached the person in charge of this in Edinburgh. This was a Professor Steven, who had been seconded to Edinburgh for this particular job. I knew him quite well, he had been in the Forestry Commission at the same time as I was, in the early 1920s, a bit snobbish and very academic in his outlook towards the workers and working foresters, which didn't just suit me. However, he was the man in charge and I had to approach him. The headquarters office in Edinburgh was controlled in a way by the Forestry Commissioner, Sir Samuel Strang Steel. Of the seven regions in Scotland the one to which I was appointed was in Grantown-on-Spey. This is on the Seafield estate, at that time just about the biggest estate in Scotland, or in Britain for that matter. Its castle was surrounded with woodlands, quite near the small town of Grantown-on-Spey.

When I arrived there I met the man in charge, L.E. McIver, the Divisional Officer. The set-up for this particular home timber supply was exactly the same as the Forestry Commission's. There were Divisional Officers, and the equivalent of District Officers, called Works Officers. As a Works Officer I came under L.E. McIver. He had an office in Grantown-on-Spey, in which I had one room. McIver had to introduce me to the work in which I was going to be involved, though I don't remember him going out into the forest to introduce me to the work on the ground. I did, however, meet two of the men who were in charge of the actual local field work, called foremen. There was a third one, but I don't remember meeting him. There was only one sawmill for the whole batch of work McIver was doing, and I met the ex-Forestry Commission forester who was in charge of it. The other man I met was dealing with extremely valuable old Scots Pine timber, and he was an ex-forester as well. In both cases they had no experience of dealing with timber and its production, though they knew something about forestry. When I arrived it was pretty chaotic everywhere.

My first job was to see to the mature timber – handling that mature highly valued timber, old Scots Pine, great huge logs worth, if not their weight in gold, certainly a great deal of money at that time. I wanted to make sure that timber was being handled correctly. It was sent south in log length and was used for extremely valuable ship building purposes. It had to be felled very carefully and processed so far by cross-cutting at the correct length and at the correct diameter for export south.

I got the man set up and was satisfied he would carry on in the correct way. The sawmill was the usual Scotch two-bench mill, a temporary sawmill reasonably well used. It was under this ex-Forestry Commission forester who, I am sorry to say, had been demoted in the Forestry Commission for being an alcoholic; he was not dependable. The men in the sawmill were quite reliable and could be left on their own, but the foreman was not, and one could do very little about it because there was so much other work.

The third unit, so far as I can remember, had no foreman in charge. The man in charge was in fact dealing with the establishment of camps of workers. This particular unit was one in which we had a batch of men from Northern Ireland, with absolutely no experience whatsoever in the handling of timber. They were set up in a camp of wooden huts. They were set to work in the woodlands, simply felling timber, snedding it and leaving it, or cross-cutting it into lengths to be handled as pit props later on. They were doing no processing at all.

A fourth unit was being set up, a very strange one, one I didn't think it was possible to have at all. McIver had arranged with a local timber merchant to handle in his own sawmill timber supplied by the Department ready for sawing. It was cut into lengths suitable for mining timber and had to be measured in those small pieces at the saw bench, instead of being measured at the site as standing timber, and then sold to the timber merchant to handle in any way he wished. The measurement of that timber at the saw bench was an absolute nightmare. That was the arrangement between McIver and the timber merchant, I didn't interfere with it at all. I had very little to do with that particular unit.

A fifth unit was being set up, of standing timber again. The timber in these woodlands, apart from the highly valuable timber I have already mentioned, was not of any size, it was really only fit for pit props. This unit was to fell, cross-cut and transport the timber to be processed. It was here that McIver and I fell out over transporting the timber. I felt I was doing war work, but it wasn't much use trying to carry on with a man who had such opposing views from mine in regard to the handling of timber, so I told him I was leaving.

There were other aspects of his way of working and way of life which didn't suit me at all. I felt he had an extremely bad influence among his workers. He was, like the forester I mentioned, an alcoholic, and was most undependable. In view of that I handed in my resignation, and that was the end of my short period at Grantown-on-Spey.

Besides the difficulties with McIver which I found insuperable, I had my wife with me, and we were living in rooms which were comfortable enough but it wasn't a life I wanted to continue for any length of time. I could see that this wasn't a six months' job, it could go on for years, and I couldn't see any prospect of getting a house. So we came south. Looking back over my short period in Grantown – I don't think I was there more than a month or two – there were two incidents which were very happy ones. One was being in touch with a substantial Newfoundland set-up for timber production, on the same extensive estate. These Newfoundlanders had nothing to learn. They had a mechanically driven sawmill, the best transport I have ever seen for extracting timber, the most modern felling tools and were themselves expert.

The other happy incident was when a batch of schoolboys came with their teacher from Glasgow, boys of 14, 15 or 16 who were very bright. I had to show them what they were to do. They were to fell quite small timber, pitwood timber, and of course they knew nothing about it. I showed them how to saw down timber, then to snedd it and to prepare it for transporting in the full length in which it was to be processed. I was surprised at the skill with which I was able to show them this job, as I hadn't used an axe or saw for years. They had to be advised how to handle an axe, to make sure they wouldn't be hurt in any way. They were very smart and picked it up very quickly. The teachers were in charge and one of them and I became very friendly and we kept up with each other for several years after he went back to Glasgow. I was quite sorry to have to leave these boys and their teachers; they had got down to the job properly and were doing excellent work.

When I left Grantown-on-Spey I should think I informed Steven in writing that I was giving up the job. I knew I would be under a cloud, and I certainly was for a long time after that. I was unemployed, I hadn't asked for a transfer, but in time I did get back into the home timber supply service again. This time I was appointed to Perth, where the regional office was under a very different man from McIver. Frank Scott was not teetotal like me, but he was next door to it. I had met him once or twice when we were both in the Forestry Commission in the 1920s. He came from Perth, but my headquarters were in Forfar. Belle and I got rooms in Forfar itself, temporary rooms, I hoped, which were the best I could get just at the beginning. There was little hope of getting a house at any price. Perth and Angus, particularly Angus, were swamped with Poles. Every corner was handed over to Poles and those of us outwith the Polish community got no consideration at all.

The headquarters of the Perthshire/Forfar region were in Perth, and Scott had a great chunk of Perthshire to do, and into Fife and Angus. My section was really in Angus and just on the end of Perth. In fact, one of the units was in Perth, on the edge of Angus, and one was close to Alyth. This was in the charge of a man there who had a sawmill and also another section which was a breast-bench, a cross-cutting bench for preparing nothing but pit props. He had sawmill staff, a felling staff, extraction staff and an office with a girl in it.

He also had a number of girls. There was a training camp in Angus with about twenty girls in it, in a big house not far from Brechin which was the nearest town. Here girls were trained for work in the forest. These twenty girls had to do three or four weeks' training. There was a woman there who had full charge of them. I had to train them in the field, a job quite new to me. I had to give them the best training possible in the short time they were there. A new group must have come in at the time I arrived and I went to see them working throughout their training period. They were in charge of a foreman, quite a clever lad and very helpful; he was very glad to see me and we got on well together. I can never forget seeing these girls going home at night, dead beat and hardly able to walk, after working a whole day from 8 in the morning until 5 at night, using axes and saws which were quite new to them. It beat me to know what to do, but I made up my mind there and then that I would make a big change. Those girls were nearly all town girls, I only met two, out of all the dozens I came across, who were country girls and could look after themselves, more or less. These town girls were fresh to the country, fresh to this kind of hard manual work, and I made up my mind that they should not have to work a whole day for the first week for their training period. I saw the woman in charge at the hostel and told her they should not come out until midday, the forenoon was to be taken as a period of rest. They were only to work the afternoon for the first solid week of their training period. After that they would have to work the full number of hours. It must have made a difference to those girls because half a day's work straightaway was quite sufficient for them.

I took charge of three units under Scott and in time matters changed completely and my field work became much easier. A later unit was formed on an estate near Forfar which belonged to a doctor and his wife. Later on I became very friendly with this doctor. Up to this time my wife and I had taken lodgings in Forfar. When we came to this unit there was no accommodation, and we were still living in Forfar, but I had to make some change. When I came to the estate of Newbarns I got permission from this doctor to be allowed to have a caravan set up in a corner of his estate. This he allowed and we had three to four years living in a caravan which we hired. It was a small caravan – the big caravans were hardly in existence – but it was reasonably comfortable and in time I attached it to a small shed which helped to hold some things which couldn't be held in the caravan. It had a dry closet.

We had working units with a considerable amount of female labour which I proved conclusively was not very effective. The people in Edinburgh insisted on having a women's unit on its own. In the end I had to agree to this. I didn't see much point in it, perhaps that might be considered one of the reasons why in the end it failed. We did set up a unit under a foreman, the unit had to be 100% women, and I had to select two women to take control. I selected the two country women I've already referred to as being the only able women who could take control. They didn't get a full sawmill business to tackle but they did have to have a saw bench for cross-cutting props. This unit was set up in the middle of quite easily handled timber where they felled it, cross-cut it, snedded the branches and then brought it to the saw bench to be sawn into pit props. They did manage to do this work quite well, but they had to do the whole thing – felling, extraction with tractors, saw bench work, preparing props and stacking them in their proper stacks, and then seeing to despatch to the station for sending to the mining areas. They got into difficulties many times, particularly in extraction. Although I was not supposed to take any help from the men to assist in this I had many times to draw a man in to help them out with the extraction part of the job. The extraction over very rough ground was an extremely difficult operation and one which required high skill. In the end this side got so difficult the unit had to fade out and in the end it was closed down. I wasn't sorry because it was always a worry to see them held up in this particular way, but in the end it had to go. The Edinburgh people who were very keen on it had to accept this. Strang Steel who was at the top of the business in Edinburgh was very keen on this particular women's unit, I think because a relation of his was in charge of all the units in Scotland and I think she wanted to prove conclusively that women were just as able as men in this particular work. I am afraid I got under her skin, because I got the name of being "the beast", and I was known as "the beast" in Edinburgh and perhaps all over Scotland. Yet I was the one who really stopped the beastly treatment of girls when they came fresh from Edinburgh or Glasgow.

During this period Scott had not interfered with me, I hardly ever saw him. I did get to know him intimately, and we became very close to each other. He retired at his age limit, when he was just over sixty, in fact, sixty-three, and went to live in Blackford in Perthshire. He was replaced by a man who had been in the forestry service in India, a forester with a forestry degree. Scott was like myself, just an ordinary working forester without a degree although he had had one year's training in forestry when he was in the Botanics, doing the same course as I had done. This man Moodie who replaced Scott was an Englishman. I liked him very much indeed. He was a very much more forceful man than Scott, and that forcefulness appealed to me very much, just as, I think, my forcefulness appealed to him. We got on very well together and he was there to the very end of the war.

Now I came to the end of my Board of Trade experience. I had had a wide experience on which I look back with mixed feelings of joy and sadness, sadness on looking back on the Grantown unit under McIver and joy on looking back on my work in Perth and Angus, particularly that along with Scott and Moodie in charge.

So once again, for the second time, I finished with the aspect of forestry I disliked in many ways, that is to say, the felling of timber and its production in sawmills. The main objective of my life was the building up of forests, establishing communities involved in the production of timber and in forestry. To this end I approached the Commissioner who was in charge of the Board of Trade timber supply department in Edinburgh, Strang Steel. I wrote to him asking if he would help me get back into the Forestry Commission, as I wouldn't go back to private estate work at any price. However, Strang Steel wasn't sympathetic at all. He wrote back to tell me that I was not equipped for taking over any forestry responsibilities at all, inferring that I should try for forestry work in some other way, say private estates. I then went to the man in charge of forestry in Scotland, the assistant commissioner in Edinburgh, a man called Gosling. I had to go to Edinburgh to take back my car, and while I was there I made a point of trying to see Gosling direct. I just went to his office and knocked on his door. We had a few minutes talk, and he said he would consider it and let me know. He did let me know: I was told there was no work for me with the Forestry Commission ever – I got the word "ever" quite clearly. The Forestry Commission was at that time involved in a huge expansion. They had done, during the whole of the war, no planting whatsoever, and were now being pushed to extend this work so as to give employment to as many people as possible after the war. In view of this the lack of senior men with experience was tremendous, and I felt there was a need for men such as myself. However, I wasn't taken on; I was unemployed and felt quite at a loss to know what to do.

One thing that did turn up was the Forestry Commission's Census of Woodlands covering all private estates in Britain with woodlands of five acres and over. A young man named Alec Mackenzie, who knew all about me and whom I knew very slightly, was put in charge of Scotland and approached me. He asked me if I would take charge of a certain section of Scotland to cover this census. I was delighted to do it. My first section was in Angus, where I was appointed to take full charge and given an assistant and an official car. Besides that, we had to have someone who would deal with the 6 inch maps which were used for the survey purposes. I got 6 inch maps covering the whole of Angus straight away, and these were used as a basis on which to record the material required for the census. We had to show on these maps the area of each woodland on each private estate.

My wife Belle did the office work all the time I was on the survey. She proved to be very clever in using a very intricate instrument, a planimeter, which measured every area marked on each map and the acreage. The survey involved a great deal of field work. Anything less than five acres was ignored, that section came later, with another method of totalling. It also meant very fast work. I found there was no difficulty at all between the landowners and ourselves, indeed very seldom did they appear.

I completed Angus which was not too difficult, being fairly level. My impression of Angus was mixed, but on the whole it was not satisfactory. I haven't come across one area of woodland in Scotland that I consider to be well-managed. I am not satisfied with woodlands unless they are highly managed, 100% of every acre under trees. This is necessary from every point of view: money making, building up the community through forest industries, and the rest of it. Angus was not the poorest in Scotland, indeed Airlie estate was probably one of the best. It is one of the biggest in Angus, some 32,000 acres of woodland, which were reasonably well kept. Strangely enough, some of the estates, even smaller estates, had a full-time head forester, but Airlie estate with its 32,000 acres or so had no head forester. It was managed by the factor, which is all wrong, as he is not on the ground at all. It disappointed me to find the estate so carelessly looked after.

During the last war I had done a lot of work in Angus with the timber supply department and that work confirmed what I state now: that a great area of the woodlands in Angus and on private estates was very far from being well managed. Dalhousie was one, a big estate of 41,000 acres, not all woodland. Together with Airlie they made up 70,000 acres, a big total out of such a comparatively small county. On Dalhousie I found acre after acre a complete failure. Woodlands that should have been carrying a sitka spruce crop of anything up to 18,000 cubic feet per acre in forty years time were carrying rubbishy big old hardwood trees. The Earl of Airlie and the Earl of Dalhousie, with land to that extent, allowing it, in woodlands anyway, to go to waste! Talk about scandal! I had to go over all the other smaller estates, and the impression all over Angus was similar to that of Dalhousie, poor, miserable wasted land.

Further north I did a small skelp of Kincardineshire, adjoining the Angus section. Here the only estate of any importance was Fasque, belonging to the Gladstones, the same family as Gladstone the Prime Minister. He may have been out here with his axe – in my *Who Owns Scotland?* I have referred to him as the Axeman Landowner. This estate was in the region of 40,000 acres, a huge chunk out of Kincardineshire. The woodlands on the estate were reasonably well managed, but the wrong species, from the point of view of a money making industry, was planted. They were entirely under Scots Pine and European Larch.

I now come to my own home county – or calf county if you like to call it that – of Perthshire, this huge county of 1,600,000 acres. In the earlier stages, where the estate were smallish, my assistant and I worked more or less together, using the government car for transport. We covered these areas in the same way as in Angus and Kincardine, but it took much longer because of the extent of the estates. Finally we had to split up. My assistant had to go to the west of Perthshire, and I kept the car because I had to wander round many more estates to the east. We did in time get over the whole of Perthshire, a very big affair compared with the small county of Angus and even smaller section of Kincardineshire. We had no help whatever from a single owner or factor until we landed on the Duke of Atholl's estate. There the factor, a Mr. Patterson, was in charge and, when I approached him on the matter of inspecting his woodlands, I got a very different response indeed. He had completely surveyed all his woodlands and had marked them on to the 6 inch maps. Whether he was anticipating, as a forward-looking factor should have been, this survey or not, I don't know, but this help from the factor made no end of difference. I did this particular estate entirely on my own, and the help I got was just out of this world. Even so, I had to go over the whole of these woodlands on foot, and had to sum them up in the ways necessary for the census: the species, the quality of the stands, etc.

They had been noted as the people who made such a fuss about the use of their larch woodlands, and particularly that of their own creation, the hybrid larch, the cross between the Japanese larch and the European larch. The hybrid larch was the result of natural cross-fertilisation between the two species, there was nothing deliberate about it. They weren't in fact the people responsible for finding it. The man who found it was a Mr. Murray, forester on an adjoining estate, many years before, but the Atholl estates made a big fuss about this particular species. It was certainly fast-growing, but not of the quality of the European larch, and the extent of land planted by the Dukes of Atholl with hybrid larch was just short of being a scandal. In forty years time it would reach up to eighty feet or more, but the crop was such a thin one it didn't produce more than three or four thousand cubic feet, Hoppus* feet, per acre in the forty years time. I don't know how many thousands of acres he had, but the great bulk of his woodlands consisted of this favourite of theirs. I, on the other hand was looking for sitka spruce. I found one group of spruce trees with perhaps the odd silver fir. I also found a dozen or so of sitka spruce at about sixty years of age and they were so outstanding that I measured them very carefully, and I found that in forty years time, instead of a mere three or four thousand cubic feet, Hoppus feet, per acre, they would have been giving a return of anything up to eighteen thousand cubic feet per acre. The Atholl estates were wealthy enough without considering timber, but if they had been considering it and depending on it for a living, they would have slipped up badly.

The rest of the woodlands were just the ordinary run of the mill, again I can say quite confidently that I didn't find any one estate where the woodlands were anything near being top grade. There were some other huge estates, such as Drummond Castle, with pretty extensive areas of land under trees. Scone Palace was another which had extensive woodlands, and there again the management of woodlands was extremely poor and confined almost entirely to Scots Pine. It was quite evident from what I had seen all over these areas so far that game – pheasants, grouse – predominated and this determined to a considerable extent the nature of the woodlands they planned to grow. The spruces, sitka spruce particularly, were not suitable for game. They had to be grown close, to be fit for industry and sale, and sitka spruce close grown is not fit for pheasants or human beings to enter. Norway spruce is not quite so aggressive as the sitka, but there was no Norway spruce of any consequence on these properties. The reason for this – and people don't like to be told this – was the blood sports of grouse, red deer, roe deer, pheasant shooting. That applied to all the estates in Perthshire, in fact to all the estates in Scotland.

After Perthshire was completed we moved down into Fife, where I had only a small area to do. The same applied to Kinross which was a very small

*Hoppus – a method of measurement of cut timber.

county with one or two biggish estates. I use the word biggish because the estates there were nearly all under the ten thousand acre category. Kinross did not take very long, and when we finished there that was the end of our survey of woodlands for the census. It meant now building up on the maps and that had been carried on by Belle.

The map recording by planimeter of the acreages in all the woodland areas we surveyed were covered by my wife's work in the office. The field work was certainly a very big job, but, again, there was a colossal amount of work carried on in the office by planimetering, measuring, every acre of all the woodlands over five acres. I was really amazed at how my wife got on with it, because she had no background of that kind at all. She must have been pretty clever in doing that kind of work, calculating all the figures, they never came back on us as having any huge errors. Alec Mackenzie, who was in charge of the whole operation in Scotland, collected these maps from time to time. Finally, he collected the last ones, and that was the end of our share in the census of woodlands in Scotland, a pretty big share, covering two or three million acres. There are nineteen million acres in Scotland, so we covered a fair chunk of it in Perthshire.

The Forestry Commission reports based on the census are in the main concerned with private woodlands. The first was in 1924, there was this one in 1947/49, and one later in 1965/67. They impress one with the amount of work that the Forestry Commission took in hand, particularly in 1947/49. The results of that survey are the most condemnatory piece of evidence that anyone could have about private enterprise, private estate ownership, which applies particularly to forestry. It doesn't give any hope of having got anything like full production out of the agricultural aspect. The total area of woodland in Scotland in private enterprise was 1,300,000 acres, the total for the unproductive area was 647,000 acres, showing an unproductive area of over 50% of the land supposed to be in woodland.

A third census came out in 1965/67 which at one hundred pages is not quite so extensive as the two hundred and sixty-four pages of the 1947/49 census. It is quite important to record that there has been a slight improvement in private estate management of woodlands, but so small and slight that it is really negligible. We are now twenty years beyond that: whether there is much difference in the attitude of the private estate people or not I am not aware, but it is said they are taking notice of real management of woodlands, and are now following suit in regard to the planting of sitka spruce, but they have a long way to go before they come up to and keep pace with the work of the Forestry Commission since it started in 1919. Quite recently I got figures from the Forestry Commission on the area of sitka spruce in their forests. Out of around one million acres, six hundred thousand are under sitka spruce, something of the greatest value in the economy of Scotland.

Chapter 9

Consultancy

AFTER COMPLETING MY WORK with the Forestry Commission on the census of woodlands sometime in 1948, I was again unemployed. I had no idea what I would be tackling in the future at all, but I had been in close touch with Frank Scott all this time, and he had, when he retired in 1943 or so, developed a fairly substantial amount of consultancy work, some of it so big that it overwhelmed him. He asked me if I would come in and help him with it, which I was only too glad to do, and I was once again in work and earning a living. He was asked to plan a very big scheme of planting up a proposed new catchment area for the Dundee water supply. That was the job I was given by Scott: to survey the land and make suggestions as to what should be done with regard to afforestation.

That job gave me the feeling that there might be a future in consultancy and Scott and I began to work together, which we did closely for many years. I gradually began to find work in consultancy through him, and also directly, because I was beginning to have a reputation for being able to do quite responsible work, particularly for private estates, in valuing and selling timber.

I mention later the Cooperative Forestry Society of Scotland. A panel was formed just after the Second World War, of six skilled and experienced foresters, to cover the whole of Scotland. Frank Scott became a member, and put my name forward to become a member of the panel and I was selected. The panel was under the charge of a man called Bruce Urquhart, who was a landowner in Aberdeenshire, and the six of us covered the whole of Scotland. I had charge of the area where I was living, in Perthshire – I had not yet come to Rosemount – with a bit of Angus.

This panel turned out to my mind to be an extremely strange affair. We met with the Board of the Cooperative Forestry Society which consisted entirely of landowners or their factors or lawyers, eight or ten men. They sat at a table with their chairman, Strang Steel, at the head, with his game leg in a sling over a chair. We foresters were kept well away from the table, in the background. The only two of the Board I remember were Sir Samuel Strang Steel and Lord Cawdor. For our payment we made up our bills to the estate for the work done in two distinct ways. There was work on time, such as on working plans or other kinds of advisory work, and there was a set scale of fees for the Commission we got from the sales of timber. This was a sliding scale, high if the sale was only a few hundred pounds, lower, quite moderate, when it came to several thousand pounds. We had nothing to do with charging this up to the landowner. The sales were passed through to Bruce Urquhart at headquarters. The Cooperative Forestry itself determined the scale, it charged the whole account to the estate and we got a 10% return on the amount of money the estate got from the sales.

I was given a pretty big job in Angus with a general who owned some land there, quite a decent chappie. He wanted his woodlands looked over properly, particularly for sales of timber. I built up a selection of timber for sale, indicating what should be sold and what held on to. I followed this up with a valuation, a measurement of the trees and the volumes of the timber to be sold. I expected that I would go forward with the actual advertising and selling of it, and get my 10% commission. That didn't happen. Bruce Urquhart came in and said he would take over my figures, use them and do the remainder of the work. I took exception to this, and this rebellion on my part sparked off fireworks and I was suspended for six months. The panel saw what was in the wind, came out in support of me and said, "If McEwen goes, then we go also." The Board at once agreed to withdraw my suspension and I was taken on the panel again. I was supposed to make some deep apology and though I did regret having created that amount of trouble, there was no apology. I said only a few words, they waited for more, but I just sat dumb and they just had to accept the fact that I was one of the panel again.

However, the breakaway didn't stop there. Scott and I finally just stood up and said we were not staying any longer on the panel. The other four men were then told that they had nothing more to do with the Board of this Cooperative Forestry Society and the six of us were out on our own. We weren't a bit dismayed and immediately formed our own society, The Society of Consultant Foresters. Each one of us kept the same area of ground he had had when he was on the panel, and we went on for several years in this way quite happily. The Society of Foresters of Great Britain formed a panel of their own, and approached us as a consultant foresters' society to see if we would link up with them in any way at all. This was discussed very thoroughly at one of our meetings and it was decided that no action would then be taken to join up with these people. The Society of Foresters – of which I was a founder member – was a conceited kind of affair. Those with degrees became fellows straight away, the rest of us were ordinary members. I had a big fight later on to break this monopoly, and again they had to yield, and those of us who had been there for a considerable length of time and were capable foresters became fellows as well. I did become a fellow.

Scott and I went on independently, getting our own clients from the different estates in Scotland. We covered the whole of Scotland because there was no restriction as there had been with the panel. We had no difficulty in getting work. Scott was at the point of retiring; he did retire in 1953, I think, he was ten years older than I was. He retired soon after we became independent consultants and I then became practically the only one left as a consultant, though some of the others may have done some independent consultancy in their own sections.

I didn't want to wander over Scotland, I wanted to restrict myself to Perthshire, Angus and Fife, and Kinross as well. I did do a little extra work sometimes in the adjoining county of Kincardineshire and once I went into Sutherland and Ross-shire, and once into Mull, but that was all. I had plenty of work in the four counties and have a complete diary record of my work in the 1950s, 60s, 70s and into the 80s.

[John McEwen then carried out valuations for a number of estates, among them Novar, Raith, Strathenry, Ardargie, Ledlanet and the Meggernie Estate. The subsequent court case over the Novar landowner's proposal to pay the Valuation fee by instalments is referred to in *Who Owns Scotland?* Then followed commissions from the landowners of Kindrogan in Perthshire and Balnaboth in Angus, and a number of valuations for Lord Dundee. The National Coal Board, to John's delight, put in a bid for the Kindrogan timber.]

The N.C.B. had a section in Fife which dealt with buying and manufacturing timber for their own use for mining purposes. I approved of it no end – I was in favour of nationalisation and here was a nationalised industry interested in manufacturing its own material instead of buying it through the home timber trade. I didn't favour them in any way, the price I had fixed was the price I wanted to get and nothing would stop me from getting it if I could. There were two reasons why I was mud in the eyes of the home timber trade: firstly, I was demanding and getting prices which they had never thought of paying; and the other reason was the fact that now the N.C.B. were coming into the market I was selling large quantities of timber direct to them. The N.C.B. came into the picture quite seriously for me because I was just next door to Fife, in Perthshire, and also I was in Fife itself where I did sell a lot of timber to the N.C.B. The biggest sales I had were in Perthshire, this one of £37,000 on Kindrogan was the biggest one I made to them anywhere. We got very friendly and I was able to put lots of timber to them, not underhand in any way, but I didn't advertise very much.

The people who were in the Coal Board were very friendly, they were different from landowners. They were working people, in charge of the operation of buying and manufacturing timber and we got so friendly that I was asked to go to Mull to help them buy a lot of very valuable timber, mostly larch, which was more valuable than Scots Pine. I did go to Mull. My wife came with me because she was very frequently with me in the booking up of measurements. They treated us like princes. We got the best bedroom with bathroom attached in one of the biggest hotels on Mull, the Western Isles, I think, was the name of it, just outside Tobermory. It was winter, and they were able to give us this room which was a very comfortable one. We needed it because the weather was rough, we were away from home and the work was quite hefty. At the end of the day we did a valuation, and the N.C.B. bought the timber on my valuation. There was a local timber merchant who had been in the habit of buying the timber from that estate in Mull, and all the other estates on Mull, and I gathered he had a very sore feeling when he found that the timber he was able to buy at any time on his own figures had now bypassed him and was sold to a nationalised industry. That was the only time I was asked to do that kind of work for the N.C.B.

I am going to refer now to one of our really big and important landowners in Perthshire, the Duke of Atholl. The estate totals 140,000 acres at the present time. At one time it was bigger, but it has been reduced somewhat. I have had a lot to do with this particular estate one way or another. During the war the home grown department had very considerable areas of fellings on this estate for the Board of Trade supplies of timber. I wasn't concerned directly with that, but when I was left to clear up at the end of the war, this was one of the areas which came into my survey. I got to know it fairly intimately even in that short period of time. My second contact with that estate was during the census of woodlands. The present laird, plus one or two recent Dukes, had crazy ideas about land use. One was concerned with timber growing. I have already referred to the vast areas of larch which had been planted there – they were crazed on that particular species. I think the estate still has that idea, but maybe they are changing somewhat and introducing the only tree which will be of any use, the sitka spruce. The other crazed idea was game. The present Duke is daft about game and his pet game animal is the fallow deer, though the red deer is there too. He has developed the herd of fallow deer so much that these animals are now escaping from Atholl property and invading the countryside right down through Perthshire to within 10 or 12 miles of Blairgowrie. There is a new scheme of chalet building on one estate adjoining the Atholl properties where the people are just tormented with this invasion of fallow deer. It is impossible to fence them out.

I have spoken about those ideas in the minds of the owners of Atholl properties as being crazed, but if one goes further back, 50 or 60 years, what they were doing was not crazy but evil. There was a crofting community in Glen Tilt up to that time but the Duke then made up his mind that he wanted this for his blood sports and he really cleared Glen Tilt completely of its entire population of crofters.

I had always been desperate about nationalisation and did my damnedest to get all I could for the Commission on the estates in the four counties on which I was working. I got a certain amount of land, in small quantities, perhaps 500 acres and upwards. 7,000 acres was the biggest, the next was about 3,500 acres, and altogether I was responsible for getting to the Forestry Commission during my period of consultancy some 15,000-17,000 acres, none of it waste land, all of it top grade land for planting purposes.

I had established my consultancy business fundamentally towards the end of the 1950s, and I built on that foundation, with the addition perhaps of other smaller estates. The 1960s were the busiest decade of my lifetime, I think, and I was earning a very considerable annual salary. In fact, perhaps for three years in the mid-60s I paid supertax. I was quite busy at the end of the 60s when it began to fade somewhat. I had been able to save some money, which was banked and invested, and I could afford to take some relief. I felt I was secure to the end of my life. I retired in 1977, and gave up all thought of doing any more work in consultancy Other things were taking up my time and thought. Before discussing these, there are three things I should like to mention.

The first is my chairmanship of the Royal Scottish Forestry Society. In 1854 a group of Scottish head foresters on private estates considered and planned the formation of a society for Scottish foresters, which was carried out in that year with its first President, a Mr Brown, head forester on the Earl of Seafield's extensive estates at Grantown-on-Spey. Mr Brown acted as President of this new society but the fact that it was controlled by working foresters did not suit the powerful landowning ruling class and the second President was a landowner from across the border. This state of affairs, control by landowners, continued for the next hundred and five years.

I was appointed to the Council of the Society in 1950 for the usual three year period which gave me further insight into the back-stage workings of this so-called forestry society. For one thing the Duke of Buccleuch had just completed five years as President – three years was the recognised time in the end. Other landowners on the Council had finally to tell him to hop. However, without any consultation with the Council the following President was the Earl of Dundee, who sat for three years but was often choked off by his mates for sheer neglect of the society. These were the men who were in charge of our vital Scottish Forestry Society for over one hundred years. In 1960-61 I was proposed by a head forester and seconded by an estate factor, (both with Lord Howard de Walden, Kilmarnock Estates). This was immediately opposed by Colin Balfour of Dawyck, a leading light in Scottish forestry and by my close friend Professor Mark L. Anderson, who thought I would get smashed by Dawyck. I make no bones about it: I made every effort to get in touch with the two thousand odd members of the society by circular letter as I was determined to win, which I did. The voting was Balfour, 198, Anderson, 225, McEwen 371.

I was very proud of this appointment and worked desperately hard during my period as President. I had a rough time of it from the landowning and university members of the Council at our first meeting, but after the second one, when I took a full grip, I had no further trouble. In many ways I set a new lead, such as in radio broadcasts of Scottish forestry affairs, assisted no end by Stuart Kennedy of the B.B.C. in four broadcasts given in the first year. The fourth one, on the impact of Forestry Commission ownership of around 8,000 acres (more than half of Castle Lachlan estate) on which forestry and agriculture were correctly planned in fitting into each other, and where the small school I attended as a youngster with over twenty pupils, in 1960 was down to a point where closure was envisaged, saved the school which in two years was up to fourteen or fifteen pupils and was secure.

The second thing I want to mention is my O.B.E. in 1963 "for services to forestry". I have no idea how O.B.E.s or any such honours are obtained and this one, notified to me, as is usual I suppose, through the Post Office, came completely out of the blue. Harold MacMillan was Prime Minister at the time and I gather these higher-ups have something to do with it. We were advised to have morning dress or dark jackets. I had neither, so had to go to my tailor in preparation for my call to London. This cost me a good bit, plus the rail fare to London (why don't they give a free rail pass?), and the cost of a night there I was quite unwell at the time, and did not enjoy it from beginning to end. When I got to the Palace with my haversack I had to leave it with officials and make my way to where those being honoured were collected.

The Queen was at the time carrying her youngest son and did not conduct the ceremony. It was graciously carried out by Elizabeth of Glamis in her favourite green heathery-looking outfit. A friend, J.A.B. Macdonald was there first, I did not see his presentation, then I followed and after a few minutes I was on my way to collect my haversack and out of the Palace on my way to the station to get the 2 o'clock train for the north, but the Changing of the Guard was being performed, and I was held up till it was over. I got home, to bed to recover: a quite unforgettable day. I have never on any occasion worn my badge of honour, and now at ninety-eight I don't suppose I ever shall.

The third thing I would like to comment on briefly is the Statistical Account of 1967. I need not describe this assessment of land in all its aspects. I am deeply concerned with this effort to express a considered opinion of what our land in Scotland is producing, but I just wonder how much attention is paid to the voluntary efforts of those who try their best to make a fair report. In my case I was known as a consultant forester with some knowledge of this, to me, extremely valuable crop, mainly on land not fertile enough to be graded as suitable for a good return in agriculture, and I knew what I was looking for in the production of timber.

I had just completed the Forestry Commission survey of private estate forestry in Angus and when I was asked to carry out the work on this county, I knew I had the material in my pocket. I had just been married to my second wife, Margaret, and she accompanied me, and helped a great deal in booking my statements on plantations over practically all the forests in Angus. This forestry report was published in the New Statistical Account.

Chapter 10

Life in Blairgowrie

[After years in temporary accommodation John McEwen and his wife decided to settle in Perthshire, and finally bought an acre of land, for £70 or £80, on which he built a small house, to his own specifications, and designed a labour-saving garden, with water-lily pond, rockery, and an orchard of some 28 or so apple trees of different varieties, and a glass house in which he grew two varieties of peaches. His wife, Belle, and he settled here in 1950, and after her death John, then about 80, resigned himself to a lonely old age. However, at a Fabian School in Aberfoyle in 1966 he met Margaret Millar, a humanist and Labour activist from Aberdeen. At table he was placed beside Margaret and as he says:]

I HAD BEEN A MEMBER OF THE Fabian Society for a considerable number of years, and was always keen to attend one of those schools held at Aberfoyle in Perthshire. We introduced ourselves and that was the beginning of our friendship. It developed, can I say, fast? We found ourselves thinking along the same lines. After Belle died I had taken a deeper interest in local politics, and I was trying to get a newspaper, or at least a newssheet, going in the Perth Labour Party. It was taken up quite seriously by some of the leaders in Perth, and a small committee was formed to thresh out what should be done with the newssheet. This was one matter I raised with Margaret. She said that they had in Aberdeen a paper, *The Clarion*, a newssheet similar to the one I was thinking about, and she would get me a copy of it. There was another person at the school concerned with the publication of *The Clarion*, and we were also introduced. Our friendship started there.

Margaret was half Edinburgh and half Caithness. Her mother belonged to Caithness and was the daughter of a crofter, nor far from John O'Groats, her father belonged to the upper middle class. His father was one of the very big building contractors in Edinburgh, doing extremely expensive work such as building big castles. We went up to Caithness to have a look round her area. Her closest friends were there, not in Edinburgh. We spent a couple of days there and from that time onwards Margaret and I decided to get married. We got married at the beginning of July 1967, a quiet wedding at a registrar's office. She had arranged a small company: her daughter, who is married to Bob Hughes, who was the Labour M.P. for North Aberdeen, and four grandchildren, and some friends of hers. I had no-one there on my side at all. We left there in the afternoon, and came here to Rosemount.

> [His marriage to Margaret changed John's life. He now had a ready-made family; the grandchildren often came to stay, and John was drawn into group singing, acting, and in general a more relaxed life-style. He took up painting in his eighties, as Margaret was a talented painter. They went to painting courses at Kindrogan and Blairmore Lodge. They also went frequently to the theatre, played a game of Scrabble almost every evening (which Margaret almost always won, to John's chagrin) and at an advanced age he learned not only to play bridge, but also to keep the score. He describes this new life as follows:]

I was never much involved in going to the theatre or entertainments of that sort, but after we were settled in Rowantree, Belle and I went to the Dundee theatre. I don't remember anything about the play at all, but I do remember the delightful comfort there was in that particular theatre. It didn't matter where you sat, the joy in my memory of it was the community feeling one had in that theatre. You felt it immediately you sat down, and it was very sad that this theatre went on fire and disappeared. We have been recently, since Margaret came, to the new theatre in Dundee which was supposed to replace it, and the community feeling has gone completely. The play was one of John McGrath's which we would have enjoyed very much, but the community feeling had gone and we didn't enjoy that particular play to the degree we should have done if we hadn't felt so isolated there. Margaret and I did go after that to other theatres. We went to the Pitlochry theatre, which has now moved on to better quarters, and, though the community feeling was not so deep as in the one in Dundee, it was quite pleasant and we enjoyed the theatre. We also went to the Byre in St. Andrews when we were there for a weekend, and the feeling of community was very strong there. I do not know whether much should be made of the community feeling in a theatre or not, but it did impress me very much indeed, the feelings expressed in the various theatres we attended. On television the plays that impressed me most were those by Harold Pinter. Whenever a Pinter play was on, we watched it.

I have already mentioned the books which influenced me when I was a schoolboy. I always did a fair bit of reading. Belle, my wife, also read a fair bit, simpler material than I was in the habit of reading perhaps, but she was responsible for bringing Thoreau into the house. I don't know how she got a hold of it, but it was a book that did impress me very much indeed, and it still remains in my mind as one of the books which did have a big influence on my life and thinking. This was followed by Whitman which I got for myself. This man was the one who, I think, has impressed me more from a political point of view than any other writer. He remains in my mind as an outstanding poet. I wish he could be better known, he and Thoreau, by the ordinary run of people, it would make all the difference.

Following that my reading was quite general. One book which did impress me was *Les Miserables*, it has remained in my mind all my life. Rider Haggard and H.G. Wells were two people who entered into my reading, and I have read the classics widely. I have been particularly inspired by Hardy. I have read a great many of his books, and I have been impressed by his attitude, not expressed explicitly, to the landowning class. His description of those terrible mantraps was sufficient to make Hardy one of the most important authors in all my reading.

Margaret became secretary of the Fabian Society shortly after she came here, and made all the difference in the world in managing it. She was secretary for three or four years, and helped in writing the pamphlet *Acreocracy* which I shall later refer to. She had other ways of getting to know people, among them Ann and Peter Galliard, English people, very able indeed – Peter was at the top of his profession in the mental hospital in Perth. They were very keen on organic gardening, as was Margaret. I didn't go the whole hog the way Ann and Peter did. They wouldn't touch anything that wasn't of organic origin in developing their garden. Ann in fact was responsible for forming what is now the Scottish Organic Association or Society, a Scottish affair, which has annual meetings and a publication, *The Scottish Organic Gardener*. On three occasions they came to us here in Rowantree, not long after they had started, to have a barbecue. Barbecue was a new name to me, I didn't know what it meant, but I soon found out when Peter came along with his equipment and set it up. We had between twenty and thirty people ultimately, not all organic gardeners by any means, we had friends who came along, and we had a most enjoyable evening. This organic side opened up a new social life to both of us, and we are quite proud of getting to know more and more people locally. Organic gardening won't die, and we will still keep up our association with them, though I am not one of their members, and I don't suppose I will ever be.

John McGrath was at the same time producing his play, *The Cheviot, the Stag and the Black, Black Oil*, and out of the blue came a request from Liz McLellan who was to be in the middle of his *Cheviot* thing, and from her brother David, who was at the time also tied up with the 7:84 Company. They didn't say what they wanted, but we had no hesitation in saying that they should come along and see us. *The Cheviot,* I think, had just been finished, and they wanted to play it on the West Coast, from the north right down as far as Barra, visiting the Outer Hebrides. Liz and her brother David came along one Sunday. I found Liz very stiff to begin with, I don't know why because she was coming to see what we could do to help her, but that changed very quickly after we began to discuss things. We were both far left in politics, and particularly regarding land ownership in the Highlands and Islands of Scotland. This drew us together at once. In the end I showed them the maps I had done, I had only the West Highland ones done at that time, and the index sheets which went along with the maps showing the exact acreage on each of the maps of each property held by the Highland landlords. That was exactly what they wanted. They took these maps away, and all the index sheets, to use them in their work on the West Coast with the play, *The Cheviot.* They returned the maps, and expressed gratitude for them, they had been no end of help to them in their work on this particular play down the West Coast. That was the end of that, but it hasn't been the end of our friendship with the McGraths. We have seen them several times since then, and become closer and closer. Our feelings towards land ownership, which I have had all my life, but which have intensified over the last ten or fifteen years, and the fact that we got the particulars of land ownership, is one thing that is common to both of us. We meet each other frequently, and are delighted every time they come. I needn't say I hope this will continue, I know that it will, we know these friendships are too deep to be broken in any way at all. I am looking forward to the time when John McGrath and I will join together in the near future in a further project to make huge changes in land ownership in the Highlands and Islands, and in Scotland.

On a lighter note: somebody has remarked that it is unusual for a man of 92 years of age to start playing bridge and make headway in it. I had played cards in many ways: Catch the Ten was the game we played in Argyllshire and in Perthshire in my early days, and I got very keen on it. It was a simple game, but with a great deal of fun in it. Then whist came along, a more serious game, and I enjoyed it too in a way. Then at the age of 92 I was induced by Margaret to take part in bridge. She is a very clever bridge player herself having played since she was at school, or at least since her teacher training. She is a very able player.

Figures for land ownership calculatd by John McEwen

OUR LAND IN SCOTLAND
How it is Owned
Total Area 19,068,807 acres

Private Owned (in round figures)

In Estates down to 1,000 acres .... 12,000,000 acres
In Estates under 1,000 acres .... 4,500,000 acres

Total: 16,500,000 acres

State Owned

Forestry Commission .... 1,895,500 acres
Dept. of Agriculture .... 445,800 acres
British Railways .... 45,000 acres
National Coal Board .... 49,000 acres
Defence .... 48,900 acres

Total: 2,500,000 acres

From *Who Owns Scotland?* 1977 ed. p 17

Chapter 11

Political Involvement

MY FATHER WAS NOT VERY CONCERNED with politics, but there is no doubt about it that his way of looking at affairs with which he was deeply concerned did affect me. He was a Liberal, a radical Liberal, a particular way of thinking that came from his family background. His father broke away in the '43 church trouble between the established church and what became the Free Church, and my father carried this on all his life. He had to keep it very quiet in Garth, and he had to be even more careful in Strathlachlan because he was an overseer then and if the laird had had any idea that he was on the extreme left wing of the Liberals he wouldn't have been long in Strathlachlan. My brother Willie and I were both forward thinking, and I am quite sure that when I began discussing socialist affairs with my father, he was influenced. At the end he was probably voting socialist and his way of thinking certainly had a very considerable influence on me all my life.

I didn't begin thinking about politics until I left school and went up to Banffshire when I took up work there in 1905. I had, of course, when I was at school in Glasgow and when I was working in Glasgow for a couple of years after school, been in touch with the MacArthur family. The father was a very radical Liberal, not a socialist but a radical, with strong opinions on politics. I hadn't got to the stage in 1905 when I was thinking about politics, nor in 1906/07 when I went to Altyre near Forres. However, when I went to Edinburgh things began to change.

As I have already said I was very churchy and in Edinburgh I entered into religious slum work. I had done none of that before because I was never in a town with such slums as there were in Edinburgh. Politically I was beginning to be wakened up as well. Around 1910, or towards the end of my period in Edinburgh, I began to learn something about the socialist movement. I had known nothing about it till that time. I had no socialist associations up till that time, but I remember buying, perhaps in Glasgow, a pamphlet by Ramsay MacDonald which cost 6d. I was then in close touch with Willie MacArthur, who was a left wing radical. There was a general election that year – I can't remember if there was a socialist contesting that constituency, but Willie and I were thinking primarily of a really radical Liberal, and there was such a candidate, a man McPherson, who didn't get into the House of Commons at that time, but got in later. The Tory candidate was Gilmour, his son was the Sir John Gilmour who was in the House of Commons till quite recently. That brought to a head my interest in politics in 1910. In the next two or three years I was beginning to get to know a little about socialism, especially through Ramsay MacDonald.

Soon after that I got in touch with the ideas of Tom Johnston, the man who wrote *Our Scots Noble Families*, through the terrific weekly paper he produced, the *Glasgow Forward*. That weekly determined where I was going in politics, and I took it all my life until it was transferred to Lord Thomson of Monifieth. There was nobody like Tom Johnston as editor, and when Lord Thomson took it over, and it just ceased to exist, it was a sad loss in my life. As soon as it went out of publication I took on *Tribune* straight away, to replace *Forward*, and have taken it ever since. It is one of the weeklies I will not dispense with.

Going back to my time at Cullen House when I was a trainee forester, there was very little political movement there, so I was surprised, in fact, amazed, at the results of the 1906 General Election when Campbell-Bannerman had an overwhelming majority on behalf of the Liberal Party. I was amazed at the response which the workers on Cullen House Estate gave to the results of that General Election. It made me very happy to find that I was not alone on Cullen House Estate on this matter.

I really began to know something about socialism in 1913 or thereby. Apart from one or two of Ramsay MacDonald's pamphlets, which cost, as I have said, 6d a time, Tom Johnston's *Our Noble Families* made all the difference to me. He dealt with the people in land-ownership through which I had come since I was a youngster, since I was born, in fact, and reading that book revolutionised my life. I also began to move away from religion. My wife and I had both been keen church-goers and when I was in Monaughty in Morayshire we used to walk a couple of miles to our church every Sunday morning, but on one occasion we arrived there and the minister got up and made an excuse for not being able to carry on his service that morning. The congregation was made up mostly of very rich farmers and he was tied up hand and foot with these people. One of the farmer's wives had become seriously ill, and he had spent so much time with her that when he came to take the service he made the excuse that he was quite unable to carry on. That finished me so far as church going was concerned. I had been a keen church-goer up to that time. The thing I did enjoy most of all was the singing in church, the old psalms moved me deeply and some of the hymns as well. However, that was the end of my own and my wife's church-going. Latterly of course I gradually got to the stage when I became a complete atheist. I am afraid Belle did not go along with me. We did not discuss it very much, but up to the end of her life she remained attached to religion, perhaps as a Christian Socialist.

Back in 1918 I had joined the Labour Party in Aberdeen. In that year the constitution of the Labour Party had been changed and individual members could join. This meant that the Labour Party was going to take prime place in the political life not merely in Scotland but in Britain. I was beginning to make contact with others in the Labour movement at that time. I was living in Skene at the time, and Aberdeen was our nearest city. I went there, not frequently, but we did go there at times, and I heard of a hairdresser in Aberdeen, John Paton, who was a left-wing socialist. I went deliberately to get in touch with him, making the excuse of having my hair cut, and though I can't say that we ever became very friendly, we got friendly enough to be able to meet up later on. I don't know why he gave up his business, but by the time that happened, we were still living in the small village of Lumsden in Aberdeenshire – I was still working in the timber trade – and he got in touch with me there. By this time he had been appointed in this northern part of Scotland as agent for the Labour Party, and he was trying to develop the Labour Party, pressing for socialism. We had quite a strong Labour Party in Lumsden, of which I was a member, and Paton wanted to come there to speak. He had a successful open-air meeting there. He left me a small book with his initials in it, *The Case for Socialism*, by Fred Henderson, dated 1920, a paperback which cost 6d, and I have held on to it. I carried that book around with me for years, in all the travelling I have done, and I still have it. I can't say I read a great deal of it now, but I got out of it what I wanted then. That was the end of my friendship with John Paton. He went later into the House of Commons and I followed his career there for years.

Tom Johnston, the editor of *Forward*, I met once when he was acting as Secretary of State for Scotland. We had formed a small society of foresters. I had, as I have said, joined the Forestry Commission in 1919, and I was the prime mover in forming a trade union in it, which covered Britain, not just Scotland, and which was pressing for increased wages and better conditions for both the workers and the working foresters. We met alternately in Scotland and England, and at a meeting in Glasgow we decided to call on Tom Johnston and see what he could do to help us to improve the conditions of the Forestry Commission's workers. Tom Johnston was quite sympathetic. We met him in the *Forward* office but he didn't think he could do very much for us, and at the end of the day we got nothing out of it.

The third person I met about this time was of the three the most outstanding man in my opinion – Joe Duncan, who was responsible for creating the Scottish Farm Servants' Union. When I met Joe first I was in Skene at the time of the 1918 General Election. He was standing as a Labour candidate against an extremely wealthy man who had made his fortune in China and who lived in Cullen. In 1918 I was asked, out of the blue, if I would chair a meeting in Skene for Joe Duncan – I was only a few months in the Labour Party and was asked to do that! I didn't know what to do because I had never attempted anything of the kind, but it was easy. I just opened the meeting and introduced Joe Duncan to it. He was a first-class speaker, more able than anyone I had met in my lifetime. He delivered his speech, and then the farmers thought they would have him twisted round their wee finger, but they had no idea what Joe was able to do. He was an able debater, but had also an intensive knowledge of agriculture, far deeper in many ways than those farmers in the meeting. He was all out for nationalisation of the land, with which I was in agreement. I had a deep-seated hatred of the hold the landowners had over us, and Joe must have felt something of the same, though not so deeply as I did.

I met him only once after that; I was back in Morayshire with the Forestry Commission, a short distance out of Elgin, and he was in Elgin. Somehow we got in touch with each other. I had a small car by that time, this was in 1928, an old Jowett which was a little topper, a two seater with a dickie at the back. I met him in Elgin, with Mrs. Duncan, who sat beside me in the passenger seat while Joe sat in the dickie declaring he had to see over the wheel, to see if I was driving carefully enough. We had a meal and a talk, and then I took them back to Elgin.

Quite recently, after we came to Rosemount, I saw an advertisement that Joe Duncan was coming to Kirriemuir to take part in a debate on land and land ownership. I made a point of going to that meeting, which was in a hall and crammed to the door. Three men were taking part in the debate. One man

I knew who was a factor for a very big estate in Ayrshire, a very able man. The other man was an owner occupier, that is to say, he owned a farm but was working it himself as a farmer. Joe was there strictly on behalf of land nationalisation, to prove as far as he could the absolute necessity for the nationalisation of the land. I was delighted to find that he and I had gone along the same lines; I was more deeply concerned with land nationalisation than ever and I found him just as deeply concerned. The factor made quite a good case, the owner/occupier a less good one, as he wasn't as clever as the other two men. Joe made the case that nationalisation was the only way for the people in Scotland to have any chance of living comfortably and not just subject to the towering power of the landowner. I was on his side, of course, and thought his case complete, but when the vote was taken the landowner's factor, speaking on behalf of the landowners, got the bulk of the vote, only two of us voting for Joe, I and an old farm servant who had known Joe for many years. I spoke to Joe for a minute or two after the meeting was finished, but he wanted to get back home, and that was the last time I met Joe Duncan, one of Aberdeen's outstanding men, particularly in the field of agriculture.

I have mentioned the fact that I joined the Labour Party in Aberdeen. In Elgin I also joined, immediately I arrived there. It was a moderate party as most villages and towns are in Scotland, not only then but also today. Elgin would have been a town of about 2,000 to 3,000 population, and the Labour movement there had the usual struggle where we were so close to the landlord, the power, that it was a mild affair. I got in touch with the Secretary of the local party, and we became quite friendly, but we were five miles away from Elgin and I had to cycle or walk into the town, so I was not in close contact with the Elgin Party.

As the Forestry Commission developed and the forests increased in number, the number of graded foresters, men who became established in the civil service, began to increase, and in Scotland I knew all of them. In fact very few people were as deeply concerned as I was with the Forestry Commission. I knew that amongst all the men I met there were only two socialist foresters and they weren't even with the Commission. I never came across one single man who admitted to being a socialist in the Forestry Commission except myself; so I was really odd man out along the line.

During the First World War wages had gone up considerably, even on private estates. The Forestry Commission wasn't in existence at that time, but when it was set up wages were still at their peak. Very soon after the war was over there was a demand for a reduction in wages, not only in forestry but in agriculture and industry as well. The men at the top of the Forestry Commission had every sympathy for this movement towards reduction, because they were important landowners, like Lovat. The reduction was from something over £2 a week to 37/- or 38/- per week. I was paying the first rate, and when it came to a reduction I took a firm stand, I make no boast about it, and said that I was not coming below £2. I got my way, and all the time I was there, up to 1928, we were still paying £2 a week. I am not sure if this affected all of forestry, but in Monaughty, Teindland and Ordiequish they continued to pay that rate.

However, we had our own fight, amongst the established foresters-in-charge. There were two grades, Grade 1 and Grade 2, later called chief foresters and head foresters. I was Grade 1. As numbers increased we got to know each other intimately. I had spent most of my life as a working man in the home timber trade, which was a rough and ready place, but where wages were much higher than in the private enterprise forestry section. I made up my mind that we must have a trade union amongst our Scottish foresters-in-charge in the Forestry Commission, and I was successful in getting every single forester in Scotland who was with the Commission to join with me in getting in touch with the trade union movement. We became members of the Workers' Union, that is, all the foresters-in-charge, those below this were not included. We didn't at first have close contact with the Forestry Commission men over the border, but when we began to have closer contact I found there was one man doing exactly the same thing in England and Wales. This man, Meldram, had been in Canada, and come back and joined the army, and had then gone into the Forestry Commission. We got in touch and became close friends, linking up our two unions as members of the Workers' Union. We had regular meetings, mostly in London, and eventually the trade unionist in charge of the department to which we were attached suggested we should do something about improving our conditions.

We were not satisfied with either pay or housing conditions, and this trade union official arranged that we should protest to the Commission through him. The protest was so forceful that the Commission had to take action, and we had to appear in London one day in court. We spent a solid day there, threshing things out, but in the end the result was one of the most saddening things that has ever happened in my fight for better conditions. The settlement went dead against our foresters. It affected me in that my annual increments stopped. In my agreement an annual increment of £100 was stipulated for a number of years; I had had one increment before this. Now there were to be no more increments. Grade two men had a lower increment, probably of £80, and those foresters in the West Coast and England may have had two increments, but after 1926 all these were stopped.

As I have described, I was transferred from Scotland to Wales. I hadn't wanted to leave Scotland, though I am not by any manner of means a devolutionist. In fact, experience with the Forestry Commission, where we worked so closely together with the men in England, has helped me to consider that the link between England and Scotland is essential. Devolution is one of the things I simply cannot tolerate, I hate the idea of being separated from England in any way. The workers in Forestry in England and Scotland, like the miners, are exactly on the same footing, and should be bound together. So I was not happy at being transferred from Scotland to Wales.

In the General Strike of 1926 our rural movement was not much affected. The cottage we were in in Tiendland faced on to the railway line which ran between Elgin, Keith and Aberdeen. It was a fairly busy line, but during the strike it was reduced to one train a day between Elgin and Keith. It was a protest by the landowning class in that corner who wanted to show what they could do in their fight against the trade union movement. It was run by one of the local landowners, and was very much against my wife's and my own feelings. We used to go out and shake our fists at it as it passed up and down. In my mind there is an association between the strike and the Strathconas*, which came about in this way.

I had a great-aunt by marriage, an Elliot who married John McEwen, who was a minister of the gospel. I visited her very frequently and was very friendly with her. She lived in Forres, where she had many friends, one of whom was a lady who lived in a house surrounded by a small piece of land. This lady was connected with the Strathconas. I met her in my aunt's house once or twice and she mentioned that she had some problem with the trees on this piece of land, and asked if I would help her. I said I would and went along to inspect them, and advised her what to do. I didn't expect any fee, because I was doing it for a friend of my great-aunt's. In fact, foresters with the Forestry Commission weren't allowed to take any fees. However, she sent me a fee, three or four guineas or something like that, and Belle and I immediately sent it to the strike movement. So that is where the Strathcona fee went.

*Strathcona – 1st Lord Strathcona was the first chairman of the Canadian Pacific Railway and was a lesser Carnegie in the distribution of his wealth.

I have already mentioned the history of the Royal Scottish Forestry Society, and how it had fallen into the control of the landowners. The idea was mooted among the head foresters that we should form a society of our own, and in 1922 we called a meeting in Forres of every forester in the district. I think thirty or forty of us met, and the society was formed, office bearers fixed up and Matthew Feaks, who was head forester with the Earl of Moray, was appointed president or chairman of the society at that first meeting. I became secretary. We decided to have a meeting once a month throughout the whole year, and in the summer to arrange excursions to inspect and study different estates and their woodlands. For the winter we planned to have a meeting each month again, but indoor meetings with speakers, some of them our own people, some of them outsiders. We also wanted as far as possible to educate our younger foresters. We had our monthly meetings alternately between Elgin and Forres. We approached the local education authority and told them what we wanted. They agreed to support and pay for an evening class – there was no thought of a day class – and this started in the second year. Our first effort in this direction was in Forres. The course was taken by Ewan Grant, the head forester on Altyre Estate near to Forres, a very capable man who had been through the Royal Botanic Gardens' three year course and had been in actual practical field work all his life. His background was technical as well as practical. The second course was in Elgin, on similar lines. There were no other courses in forestry anywhere else except in Aberdeen or further south, and these were very successful, with ten or twelve attending, and a series of six, seven or eight lectures.

The next course was one I wanted to have in a district which had a good number of foresters in it. This was held near my own home in the Tiendland Forest, in a school near the forest and quite near Fochabers as well, though Fochabers wouldn't have suited the foresters as well as the small school near Tiendland. I think the education authority hesitated a little over having the course away from the small town, but I assured them there would be a full class available, and this proved to be the case. I was the lecturer, and we had a substantial number of members, young foresters from the Forestry Commission and from private forests as well. So these courses were one of the things the new Moray and Nairn Foresters' Society got going. They not only brought forestry more and more into the lives of our foresters in Morayshire, but brought forestry to the notice of the public, because these classes were publicised in the local papers, and the general public learned we were carrying out this work.

We also had an annual excursion for all and sundry, all the members of the society plus their wives and sweethearts or children. These started quite soon, perhaps in the second year, when we went to the Duke of Richmond and Gordon's seat, Fochabers Castle, a visit arranged by the forester there. It was quite successful, but by far the most successful was the one in the following year, when we went to Sluie on the Findhorn. The number of people who turned up was amazing, some hundred or hundred and twenty. We had sports, such as skipping for women. My first wife Belle was a first-class skipper, she could skip for evermore, and I think she must have come out top because no-one could beat her for skipping. We also had a meal there, arranged by the wives, and the children were catered for as well. We had a particularly valuable and pleasant meeting, and were very proud of what we had done. We felt quite independent of the Royal Scottish Forestry Society, which was quite jealous of us and tried their utmost to induce us to remain as members of their society. Foresters all over Scotland took note of our work, though none followed our example.

One other aspect of our work was the production of a journal. We had been going from 1922 to 1927 when this was suggested, and an editorial committee was set up, of which I was appointed the leader. We hoped it would be an annual event. In time I was able to get the assistance of a great many of our members in building up this journal. It carried on throughout the war, but in 1947 it just faded out, I don't know why, but it existed for over twenty years. I look back on it as something really worthwhile in which I took a fair share of the work, alongside those other foresters who were involved in it.

Further to the education of foresters, I have had the experience of hammering our own Scottish Labour Party on this matter. Willie Ross was in the Scottish Office from 1964 for about seven years, he was the longest holder of that office up to that time, though I think he can be beaten by George Younger. I tried to get him to support my demand for a Higher National Diploma. I think I must have hammered him so much that he got fed up with me, and sent along one of his Under Secretaries of State for Scotland, Willie Hughes, now I think, Lord Hughes. Willie Hughes arranged a meeting in Edinburgh, and invited me to come along, which I was glad to do. I found he wasn't alone, he had two Forestry Commission men from the headquarters in London, I think the headquarters of their educational department was there, and I was able to produce a syllabus for the education of our working foresters.

I am not surprised that there were no further meetings because I had been in close contact with Willie Ross, and found that he was able to fish much information out of me, but I got no return from him at all. I met him later at a conference, I think at Largs, to which I was a delegate, speaking on a resolution on forestry and land. I was waiting outside the conference hall at lunch time at the end of the morning session waiting for someone to have lunch with, when Willie Ross came rushing out with his big bag in his hand. He looked at me and said, "Aye, John, I'm glad you weren't too severe on me this time." I had no idea what he was getting at, but that was my last contact with Willie Ross. He is in the House of Lords now. He was no use as Secretary of State for Scotland and was followed by one who was even more useless, Bruce Millan

In 1950, after we came to live at Rosemount, things became easier for me, though I was working hard at my consultancy business. I was able to play a full part in Labour Party work at local and constituency level, attending meetings, canvassing, etc. I joined the Blairgowrie branch, at that time one of the liveliest Labour Party branches I have ever been in, and I have been in seven different branches. We had a very able secretary in Bill Stirling, a science teacher in Blairgowrie High School. Unfortunately he wasn't very happy in his job, and went to Fife. I became very friendly with Bill Stirling, and after he left I did not have many close contacts there. From about 1960 to 1967 I was still going very carefully, but I was getting in closer touch with the people in Perth, and on one occasion I was asked to speak to the Young Socialists. I was extremely proud to be asked, and one Sunday I went to Perth to meet one of the liveliest groups of Young Socialists I have ever come across. I don't remember exactly what I spoke about – it would have been on land use and land ownership, but the discussion was lively and the group had a strong desire to do something substantial in the Labour movement. Jim Ferguson was one of them, and his future wife Lorna, and we have since then worked closely together. Jim has taken a vital part in constituency work in Perth and was Chairman for some time. The Chairman of that meeting was Gavin Strang, now Dr. Strang and a Member of Parliament.

My quiet time went on to 1966 or 1967. My first wife Belle died in 1966, and until then I had lived very quietly with her. When I was left alone I began to think and, later on, to work extremely hard. I had been a member of the Fabian Society for several years before 1966 and, as I have related above, I went to a Fabian school in Aberfoyle, where I met my second wife, Margaret, then Mrs Millar. When I got back home one of the first things I did, I forget exactly how, was to advertise the fact that I wanted to set going a Fabian Society in Perth. We did ultimately form the society, which covered Perth and Kinross. We met here in Rowantree, fifteen of us, some of whom I already knew. I had met casually

Ken Alexander, and his wife, who was a New Zealander, and I must have written to them and asked them if they would come and join us in forming a society. They were living at that time in Callander, and could become members. They did so.

For the next ten years or so we had one of the liveliest Fabian Societies. It was not very big, membership never exceeded twenty as far as I remember, but they were all very keen on it. There's no doubt they were responsible for making it the lively little society it was. I was, however, not satisfied with liveliness, I wanted to see some research, something worthwhile for the society to tackle. It was left to the members to propose any project they could think of and finally they decided to find out about our landowners in Scotland, particularly in regard to the unemployment that was evident in Perthshire at that time, and the amount of employment that was got through the private estates in Perthshire. A small committee was set up; I should have liked to have more members involved, but the committee was formed of four of us, Jim Ferguson, Alistair Steven, Margaret and myself. Alistair Steven was the one who wrote the report, with help from Margaret; Jim Ferguson, on the other hand, found out far more about the landowners than anybody else. He had some inside information, and that was what we were really after. I was working quite hard on it as well, and in the end we were able to issue the pamphlet, *The Acreocracy of Perthshire*. We were determined to have this ready in time for the annual conference of the Labour Party in Perth, and we just did manage to have it ready on the bookstall. It wasn't a best-seller, but we certainly sold many copies, and one result of that pamphlet was evident the following year, when the Labour Party Conference was held in Inverness. At that conference there were four resolutions from four different constituencies demanding that something should be done about landownership and land use. Sandy Lindsay of the Inverness Labour Party moved the resolution and I seconded it. What we were asking for was a working party to go deeply into the question in Britain. This was unanimously accepted by the Conference, and in the end a working party was set up under the Chairmanship of Alan Campbell Maclean, a left-wing socialist in Inverness. He drew up an interim report in 1972, which was put forward to the Labour Party Conference of 1973. We looked forward to getting something quite substantial out of that working party, but sad to relate it just faded away. Nor was the Fabian Society interested, even though *Acreocracy* was the result of Fabian work. I found the Fabian Society had almost a distaste for dealing with any aspect of land at all.

There is one local aspect I must mention, in the work of the Perth and Kinross Constituency Labour Party. Davy White, Secretary of the Labour Party in Perth, was a terrific party worker, a strong character, and he approached me, knowing I was interested, and told me he was proposing to get a headquarters for the constituency. He had in view the purchase of an old semi-derelict building for which he required a certain sum of money. He said he had got £200 from one individual, and that he required another £200. I didn't hesitate, I handed over £200, and with the £400 and some subscriptions he was able to buy the small building. Davy found there was a great deal of work to be done, and I don't think enough credit has been given to him for the amount of work he must have carried out to make these quarters liveable. They were an absolute godsend to the Constituency and to the Fabian Society, which met there every month and paid 10/- for each time they used them. I got my £200 back a few years later, and the debt must have been paid off completely. I was glad to be able to help the local party buy this derelict house in Barossa Street.

It was difficult keeping Blairgowrie and District Labour Party alive over the years. It had to be resuscitated several times. Incomers to the district helped enormously, for example, Michelle and David Moody, librarians, served as Secretary and Treasurer. Robert Perks, now in the Chair of Accountancy in Belfast, also threw his enormous weight and enthusiasm behind us, I remember introducing him to the Angus glens when he stood as parliamentary candidate for South Angus.

Meanwhile, with the publication of the *Red Paper on Scotland*, we had a flow of visitors and correspondence. Among the correspondence came a long letter from the Tartan Army. This gave clear instructions on the manufacture of a bomb and suggestions as to which sections of an oil-pipeline would be best to blow up. There had been some explosions in this area. At the time I was particularly interested in the left-wing West Highland Free Press, so I sent a letter to the editor, Brian Wilson, to see if he could make a scoop (no-one had heard much of the Tartan Army) before handing it to the police. There was quite a stir over this, ending in a High Court trial in Edinburgh when I had to testify to receiving the crazy letter. After the judge swore me in he asked if my age was 88. I had to correct him as it was my birthday and I was 89. After "witty" congratulations all round, I was asked if I would like to sit to give evidence but I preferred to stand. After all I was still working most days in the forests at that time. In the afternoon the accused men had brought their New Testaments and photographs with them, all expecting to be convicted. In the event, in spite of all the fantastic security in court, it was decided not to make martyrs. Only two went to prison, and what could have been a beastly movement fizzled out. It was queer that they, and other S.N.P. members, should have approached me. I have never had any time for tartan humbug, Highland Games, any of the phoney, Victoria-inspired picture of our land. I have vigorously opposed not only separation, but also devolution.

We now live in a North Tayside Constituency of which Blairgowrie seems to be the centre. We do not attend many meetings, no car now, though members very kindly wheel us round. We still are confident that we shall have eventually a socialist government, that day will come. Friends keep asking me to state clearly what will happen then to our land, and how we shall act towards its future use. I am not afraid to reply, but it is too difficult a subject for me, or for anyone to state "clearly" what will happen. The landowners will be out, for one thing, and though there will be difficulties and trouble in the future, I hope we shall come to realise that we cannot possibly go on existing with the present-day extremes of poverty and wealth. How it will end in the near future I know not, but end it must and then we **must** go forward and **shall**.